Homophones Resource Book

Susan C. Anthony

Nature's Workshop Plus, Inc.
P.O. Box 425
Danville, Indiana 46122-0425
www.workshopplus.com

Teach with less effort, more SUCCESS!

Susan Anthony's materials are designed to help teachers maintain high objective standards while helping *all* children reach them. Nurture the excitement of learning in your students, build their confidence with early success, and build a framework of background information to which new learning can be connected throughout life.

Susan's books are available from:
Nature's Workshop Plus, Inc.
P.O. Box 425
Danville, IN 46122-0425
mail@workshopplus.com
www.workshopplus.com
Phone: (888) 393-5663
Fax: (866) 279-2505

Contact Susan at:
Susan C. Anthony
P.O. Box 111704
Anchorage, AK 99511-1704
Susan@SusanCAnthony.com
www.SusanCAnthony.com
Phone: (907) 345-6689

Books by Susan C. Anthony include:

Reference	*Facts Plus: An Almanac of Essential Information*
	Facts Plus Activity Book
	Encyclopedia Activity for use with The World Book Encyclopedia
Spelling	*Spelling Plus: 1000 Words toward Spelling Success*
	Dictation Resource Book for use with Spelling Plus
	Homophones Resource Book
	Spell Well: A One-Year Review for Older Students
	Personal Dictionary
Mathematics	*Addition Facts in Five Minutes a Day*
	Subtraction Facts in Five Minutes a Day
	Multiplication Facts in Five Minutes a Day
	Division Facts in Five Minutes a Day
	Casting Nines: A Quick Check for Math Computation

Note: Although the author and publisher have exhaustively researched all sources to ensure the accuracy of the information contained in this book, we assume no responsibility for errors, inaccuracies, omissions or any other inconsistency herein. Any slights against people or organizations are unintentional.

ISBN 1-879478-14-5

Contents

Alphabetical List of Homophones

Homophones: Fun but Frustrating!

Homophones make possible many of our jokes, puns and word games, but they are a great frustration for spellers of English! A writer must recognize a homophone, then think about which meaning fits the sentence, and finally select and write the correct spelling. This is an especially difficult task for learners, and even many adults!

Although as many as 30% of "spelling" mistakes involve homophones, computerized spell-checkers may not find these mistakes. Students must become competent in using the most common homophones. This is difficult for some, but good instruction and frequent review will lead to success. Students who have *mastered* a set of homophones will write them correctly most of the time in first drafts, and always find and correct them when editing.

This book was developed as an ancillary to the *Spelling Plus* program but will stand alone for use with any method of teaching spelling. It provides educators with resources and suggestions for teaching homophones, to be used as needed with individuals or an entire class. The proper use of these resources depends upon the professional judgment of the teacher, who must decide which sets of homophones should be introduced and when, based on the abilities and needs of his/her own students.

Whether the weather's sunny,
Whether it's cold or hot,
Whether it's raining
or snowing or blowing,
It's the only weather we've got!
So we just have to
weather the weather
Whether we like it or not!

What Exactly *Is* a Homophone?

— **Homophones** are words which have the same pronunciations but different meanings and different spellings. The Greek combining form **homo** means "same" and **phone** means "sound." So **homophone** means "same sound." Examples are: **your – you're** and **principal – principle.** Homophones cause problems for students as they encode, or transfer sound into script during the act of writing. Homophones are sometimes called homonyms.

— **Homonyms** are words which are pronounced the same but have different meanings and derivations. They may or may not be spelled differently. **Homo** means "same" and **nym** means "name." An example is the word **seal**. The word meaning a marine mammal is from Old English **seol**. The word meaning a piece of wax for sealing a document and hence the verb "to seal" is from Old French **seel.**

— **Heteronyms** are words which are spelled the same but have different meanings and pronunciations. **Hetero** means "different" and **nym** means "name." An example is the word **lead.** When used as a noun meaning a metal, it is pronounced with a short **e**. When used as a verb meaning "to conduct" it is pronounced with a long **e**. Heteronyms may cause problems for students as they decode, or transfer script into sound during the act of reading.

Why Do Homophones Exist?

— Some words were once pronounced differently, but over time came to be pronounced the same. Examples are **sew – so**, where **sew** used to rhyme with **new**, and **won – one**, where **one** used to be pronounced with a long **o** as in **lone.**

— Some words were once alternate spellings of the same word, but over time the spellings specialized with different meanings. Examples are **flower – flour** which was not finally differentiated until the early 1900's. **Then – than** began to grow apart in about 1700.

— The base words may be different, but when a common ending such as **-s** or **-ed** is added to one, homophones result. For example: **tacks – tax** and **toad – towed.**

— A shortened form of one word may be a homophone of another. For example: **bye – by** and **flu – flew.**

— Some words do not have identical pronunciations, but because of imprecise pronunciation, they are confused. Examples are: **our – are** and **whether – weather.**

— Unaccented syllables are often pronounced with a schwa sound regardless of spelling. For example: **affect – effect** and **addition – edition.**

Q. What happens when you park your frog in a "no parking" zone?
A. It gets toad away.

Q. What does your teacher say when he can't read your homework?
A. Write right!

Q. What's another name for rabbit fur?
A. Hare hair.

Q. How does your dog know that you've got something tasty in your pocket?
A. His nose knows.

Q. Why didn't our things get wet in the fog this morning?
A. The mist missed.

Q. What could you call a group of directors who are totally uninterested in their meeting?
A. A bored board.

Q. How did your visitor discover your secret?
A. Our guest guessed.

Q. What could you call writing paper that doesn't move?
A. Stationary stationery.

Q. What did the boys say when they found out they had 60 minutes all to themselves?
A. It's our hour!

How Does the Homophone Resource Book Fit into the Curriculum?

Some talented students learn to spell easily and almost automatically. Others have a great deal of trouble with the spellings of basic and commonly used words, especially homophones. Because of the inherent inconsistencies in English orthography, a person's ability to spell is less indicative of intelligence than of keen visual memory.

Nevertheless, good spelling is *very* important. Readers tend to be offended by misspellings and to judge the writer harshly for them, often discounting the ideas being expressed. All students, regardless of talent, should be expected to become *successful* spellers according to these criterion:

The primary purpose of writing is effective communication. Anything that causes the reader to pause hinders that process. Misspellings do just that.
—Harry Teitelbaum

- Acceptance of personal responsibility for correct spelling in one's own writing.
- Mastery of the most common and useful words and rules.
- A systematic and adequate method for approaching the study of new words.
- Independence in using the dictionary and memory aids.
- Recognition of regular and irregular spellings.
- An understanding of word construction, roots, prefixes and suffixes.

This book provides materials and suggestions for *introducing* homophones. Dictation allows for extended mixed practice of homophones, spellings, and other language skills.

I set aside a block of time each day for spelling and language instruction, structured something like this:
- Handwriting (later keyboarding) — 10–15 minutes.
- Spelling practice activity — 10–15 minutes.
- Introduction of a single set of homophones or a single application of a capitalization or punctuation rule as needed, but not every day — 5–10 minutes.
- Sentence dictation — 15–20 minutes. Sentences include many opportunities to apply what was just taught, as well as to review everything taught to date. This bridges toward creative writing.

A separate block of time is devoted to creative writing, during which the focus is on the writing process. The editing part of the process bridges back toward what was learned during spelling and language instruction. Learning to spell homophones easily and correctly in writing is a long process. Patience and persistence *will* pay off. Celebrate every success!

A General Lesson Plan

Preparation

— Decide on a set of homophones to teach. Base your decision, in order of importance, on the following factors:
  1. Homophones which appear on the spelling list.
  2. Words several students confuse in their own writing.
  3. Words which are troublesome for spellers in general.

  In general, no more than one new set a week should be introduced. Avoid having students proof sentences containing intentional errors until they are well practiced and very competent. There is such a great potential for confusion with these that every effort should be made to prevent possible misunderstanding and wrong impressions.

— Use the alphabetical list of homophones on p. iv to locate and scan through the lesson suggestions and worksheet.

— Decide whether you wish to duplicate the worksheet, or do an oral activity. Duplicate if necessary.

Instruction

— Write the homophones, widely separated, on the board.

— Share background information you think will help students remember and distinguish the words, such as definitions, parts of speech, and mnemonics.

— Orally provide a sentence containing one of the words. At a signal, have students point to the spelling on the board they think is correct. Discuss, clarifying any confusion.

— Repeat with more sentences, then have students provide sentences, until they can distinguish between the words and verbalize why they make the choices they do.

— Have students do the worksheet.

— Correct the worksheet together and discuss any problems or misunderstandings.

It is not the sole function of writing to represent sounds. If I receive a letter beginning "My deer sir," I have seen a vision of a horned animal before my mental ear has perceived the sound of the word.

—Henry Bradley, 1913

Review and Follow-Through

— Begin using the set of homophones frequently in daily dictation, then gradually taper off as students make the transfer into their own writing.

— Dictate one or two review homophones at the end of each weekly spelling test.

— Notice and publicly compliment correct use in writing.

— Possibly play a general review game. Have students write sentences containing homophones which have been introduced on cards to be kept in a can. When you have a few minutes of time, pull out a card and read the sentence. See who can determine which word in the sentence is the homophone and provide the correct spelling.

Dictation

Daily sentence dictation is a powerful method for ensuring that students transfer what they learn about homophones into their own writing. It is extremely unlikely that students will begin using homophones correctly as a result of a single worksheet or lesson. The "demons" such as **to – too**, **there – they're – their**, **your – you're** and **its – it's** may take months or even years to master. Extensive review and practice will be needed. I tell students that every time they have to write one of these words *for the rest of their lives* they will have to pause and choose the correct spelling.

Dictation is one of the most efficient ways to "bridge the gap" between specific skills lessons such as those in this book and natural writing. I visualize the process as follows:

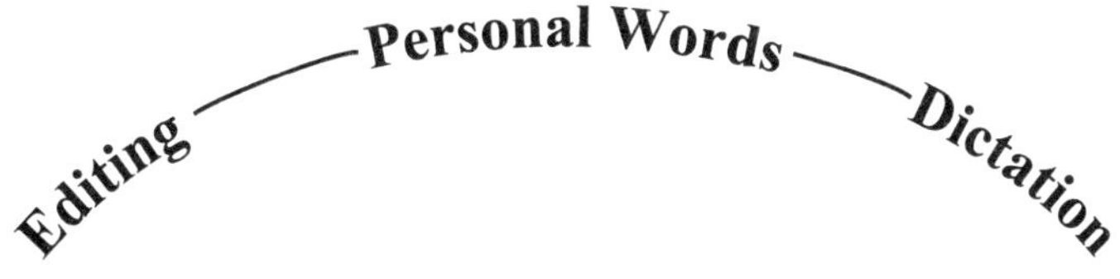

Creative	**Critical**
The Writing Process	Direct Instruction
Brainstorming	Spelling, Homophones
Rough draft	Capitalization
Sharing	Punctuation
Focus is on *Ideas*	Focus is on *Form*

I dictate, and students write, four sentences in a 15–20 minute block of time each day. I prepare the sentences beforehand to include as many homophones, spelling words and language elements as I want to review. The worksheets and lessons in this resource book each focus on a specific set of homophones. Although this is an important first step, dictation forces students to recall which words are homophones and determine which of the various spellings is appropriate during the course of writing an entire sentence. Because it is not a sentence they must create, their minds are free to focus on correctness.

Dictation provides mixed review and application of the lessons in this book, and, in time, will lead to transfer and mastery. A complete discussion of dictation is in *Spelling Plus: 1000 Words toward Spelling Success.* The *Dictation Resource Book* for use with *Spelling Plus* has sample sentences and information on incorporating language lessons into dictation. The procedure is in the sidebar to the right.

Dictation

1. **Teacher:** The sentence is: Who's your new friend?
2. **Teacher:** Say, Who's your new friend?
3. **Students:** Who's your new friend?
4. **Teacher:** Write, Who's your new friend?
   (All students write the sentence as teacher circulates around the room. The teacher may quietly repeat the sentence if needed. Use this time to compliment individual students on using good handwriting and remembering capitalization, homophones, or spellings.)
5. **Teacher** (when students are finished): Is there anything special you must remember while writing this sentence?
6. **Students:** Who's is a contraction, your, new, question mark.
7. **Teacher:** Check your papers. How many people remembered those things? If you didn't, correct now.
8. **Teacher** (writing the sentence correctly on the board and saying each letter as she writes): Capital W-h-o apostrophe s Who's y - o - u - r your n - e - w new f - r - i - e - n - d friend question mark.
9. **Teacher:** Check and correct your own papers. (When students are finished, continue with the next sentence.)

Homophones by Grade Level

Ideally, a set of homophones would be taught to an individual student as soon as the words were confused in his or her personal writing and not before. This is impractical in most classroom situations, so the teacher should select sets to teach to the group based on:

— Homophones which appear on spelling lists.
— Homophones which several students spell incorrectly in writing.
— Words which spellers in general confuse frequently.

Beware of stressing homophones too much. It is possible to cause confusion where none would otherwise exist. G. H. Vallins makes this point in his book *Spelling:*

> "Only a few homophones give people trouble, at any rate after the first stages of writing. On the whole, the more conscious we are of homophones the more we are confused by them. Some school textbooks and teachers, by artificially introducing homophonic groups to children, only tend to create difficulties where none had been or were likely to be. Luckily, the words in the less familiar groups usually sort themselves out as we grow older and more experienced. When we use one, we are not immediately conscious of the other; they do not remain associated in our minds, because we are called upon to write them on comparatively rare occasions. Only a few very common groups or pairs, like **there** – **their**, **to** – **too**, **principle** – **principal**, tempt us into carelessness, if not actual error."

The recommendations on the following page are my suggestions only. Any set may be taught in any grade at the teacher's discretion. Take your cues from student writing. This book is organized as a resource book rather than a sequential curriculum because no sequence is appropriate for everyone. Teachers are the professionals who must determine what their students most need to learn at any particular time. If students aren't confused by a set of homophones, there may be no need to teach it at all!

Recommendations are for initial instruction only. Review and reteaching should take place throughout the grades, again and again, especially for the "demons" such as **to** – **too** and **there** – **they're** – **their**. The list is provided to give teachers a general overview of what types of homophones can be taught at each level, to assist in long-term planning.

Homophones by Grade Level Recommendation

Grade 1

are – our*
be – bee
then – than*

Grade 2

ad – add
buy – by
cent – sent
for – four*
hole – whole
hour – our
its – it's*
off – of
some – sum
there – their*
there – they're – their*
to – two*
were – we're
where – were
whose – who's*
wood – would
your – you're*

Grade 3

allowed – aloud
bear – bare
beat – beet
blew – blue*
break – brake*
chews – choose
creak – creek
dear – deer
die – dye
fair – fare
fir – fur
flew – flu
great – grate
groan – grown
hair – hare
heal – heel
hear – here
I – eye
lead – led*
loose – lose
maid – made
mail – male
main – mane
meat – meet
new – knew*
no – know*
nose – knows
not – knot
oh – owe
pail – pale
pain – pane
pair – pare – pear
peace – piece*
peak – peek
peal – peel
plain – plane*
quite – quiet*
rain – rein – reign
raise – rays
read – red
reads – reeds
real – reel
sail – sale
sea – see
seam – seem
soar – sore
steak – stake
steal – steel
tail – tale
to – too – two*
toad – towed
toes – tows
waist – waste
weak – week*

Grade 4

ate – eight
berry – bury
board – bored*
buy – by – bye
course – coarse
dew – do – due
flour – flower
form – from
forth – fourth
hall – haul
hay – hey
heard – herd*
higher – hire
missed – mist
night – knight
none – nun
one – won
pause – paws
rap – wrap
right – write*
ring – wring
road – rode*
sew – so – sow
tacks – tax
threw – through*
weather – whether*
which – witch

Grade 5

addition – edition
ant – aunt
celery – salary
cell – sell
clothes – close*
desert – dessert
guessed – guest
horse – hoarse
passed – past*
profit – prophet
sense – since*
son – sun
stairs – stares*

Grade 6

accept – except*
access – excess
affect – effect*
capital – capitol
ceiling – sealing
cent – sent – scent
cereal – serial
conscience – conscious
council – counsel
patience – patients*
principal – principle*
scene – seen
stationary – stationery*
wade – weighed
wait – weight
way – weigh

*Recommended for special emphasis.

Notice that a large number of sets are recommended for third grade. This may be a good year to do a special unit on homophones, with word play, illustrations, a bulletin board, etc.

The *Spelling Plus* list is indicated if either or both words are on a list.

Recommended grade levels are suggestions *only*. Teachers decide when to introduce homophones.

Definitions are brief and include only the most common meanings and parts of speech, to help students distinguish the words from one another. For complete definitions, use a dictionary.

Background information from which teachers select what will help their students:

- Why the words may be especially confusing.
- Relative frequency, from *Frequency Analysis of English Usage: Lexicon and Grammar.*
- Meanings of word parts.
- Historical and etymological information.
- Mnemonics.

accept – except *p. 41*

Spelling Plus list 59.
Recommended for grade 6.

accept *v.* to receive willingly
except *prep.* other than, but

Both of these words come from the same Latin root. Because the first syllables are unaccented, the pronunciation is confusingly similar. Both words are used with about the same frequency.

The root **cept** means "take." The prefix **ac-** (same as **ad-**) means "toward." So **accept** has the meaning "take toward."

The prefix **ex-** means "out." Think of **exit**. So **except** has the meaning "take out."

Associate **accept** with **yes** and **except** with **no**.

Answers

1. *accept*
2. *except*
3. *accept*
4. *except*
5. *accept*
6. *except*
7. *except*
8. *accept*
9. *except*
10. *except*
11. *accept*
12. *accept*
13. *except*
14. *accept*
15. *except*
16. *except*
17. *accept*
18. *except*
19. *accept*
20. *except*

Page number on which the worksheet is located.

Answers to worksheet. As much as possible, I avoided the issue of capitalization. If capitalization will be necessary, remind students in advance.

Note: Although the purpose of these worksheets is to teach homophones, incidental learning in other areas may take place. Facts given in the sentences are accurate, and are from *The World Book Encyclopedia, Facts Plus: An Almanac of Essential Information,* and *The Guinness Book of World Records.* If students seem especially interested in a fact presented on one of these worksheets, encourage them to use reference books to find out more and share what they discover with the class.

accept – except *p. 41*

Spelling Plus list 59.
Recommended for grade 6.

accept *v.* to receive willingly
except *prep.* other than, but

Both of these words come from the same Latin root. Because the first syllables are unaccented, the pronunciation is confusingly similar. Both words are used with about the same frequency.

The root **cept** means "take." The prefix **ac-** (same as **ad-**) means "toward." So **accept** has the meaning "take toward."

The prefix **ex-** means "out." Think of **exit**. So **except** has the meaning "take out."

Associate **accept** with **yes** and **except** with **no**.

Answers

1. *accept*
2. *except*
3. *accept*
4. *except*
5. *accept*
6. *except*
7. *except*
8. *accept*
9. *except*
10. *except*
11. *accept*
12. *accept*
13. *except*
14. *accept*
15. *except*
16. *except*
17. *accept*
18. *except*
19. *accept*
20. *except*

access – excess *p. 42*

Not on the Spelling Plus list.
Recommended for grade 6.

access *n.* the right to enter or use
excess *n. adj.* more than enough

Both of these words are used with about the same frequency in English. Although they have different pronunciations, the difference may be difficult to hear.

Access comes from the Latin **accessus** which meant "approach."

Excess comes from the same Latin root as **exceed** which means "to pass the limits of."

Associate **access** with **approach** and **excess** with **exceed**. Pronounce the words clearly while spelling.

Answers

1. *access*
2. *excess*
3. *excess*
4. *access*
5. *excess*
6. *access*
7. *access*
8. *excess*
9. *excess*
10. *excess*
11. *access*
12. *access*
13. *excess*
14. *excess*
15. *access*
16. *access*
17. *access*
18. *excess*
19. *excess*
20. *access*

ad – add *p. 43*

Not on the Spelling Plus list.
Recommended for grade 2.

ad *n.* advertisement
add *v.* to join or combine, to use addition

Both of these words are directly related to longer English words.

The word **add** is used *much* more frequently in English than the word **ad**. Because of this, some children may not ever confuse these words. Teach this set of homophones only if there is evidence of confusion in student writing.

Think of **adding** an extra **d** to the word that has to do with **addition**.

Answers

1. *add*
2. *add*
3. *ad*
4. *add*
5. *ad*
6. *ad*
7. *add*
8. *ad*
9. *add*
10. *ad*
11. *ad*
12. *add*
13. *add*
14. *add*
15. *ad*
16. *ad*
17. *ad*
18. *ad*
19. *add*
20. *add*

addition – edition *p. 44*

***Addition** is on Spelling Plus list 58.*
Recommended for grade 5.

addition *n.* the act of adding
edition *n.* a version or issue of a publication

These words are confusingly similar because of the unaccented first syllables. **Addition** is used much more frequently than **edition.**

The root word of **addition** is **add.** The short **a** can clearly be heard in this word.

The root word of **edition** is **edit.** The short **e** can clearly be heard in this word because it's accented.

Overpronounce the words as they are spelled, remembering the roots.

Answers

1. *addition*
2. *addition*
3. *edition*
4. *edition*
5. *addition*
6. *edition*
7. *edition*
8. *addition*
9. *addition*
10. *edition*
11. *edition*
12. *addition*
13. *edition*
14. *addition*
15. *addition*
16. *addition*
17. *edition*
18. *edition*
19. *edition*
20. *addition*

affect – effect *p. 45*

Spelling Plus list 64.
Recommended for grade 6.

affect *v.* to influence
effect *n.* a result or outcome

Because the first syllables are unaccented, the pronunciation of these words is confusingly similar. The noun **effect** is used much more frequently than **affect**. **Effect** is sometimes used as a verb, meaning "to bring about" as in "to effect a compromise." This worksheet has no sentences in which **effect** is used as a verb.

Associate **effect** with the idea of cause and effect and **affect** with **influence**. Overpronounce the words as if they began with long vowels as an aid to spelling.

Answers

1. *affect*
2. *affect*
3. *effect*
4. *effect*
5. *effect*
6. *affect*
7. *affect*
8. *effect*
9. *affect*
10. *affect*
11. *affect*
12. *effect*
13. *affect*
14. *effect*
15. *effect*
16. *affect*
17. *effect*
18. *affect*
19. *effect*
20. *affect*

allowed – aloud *p. 46*

***Allow** is on Spelling Plus list 29.*
Recommended for grade 3.

allowed *v.* permitted
aloud *adv.* out loud

The base word of **allowed** is **allow**. Add **-s** to **allow** to form **allows** and add **-ing** to form **allowing**.

Aloud was once two words, **a** and **loud**. Stress to students that it is now one word. If "out loud" can be substituted in the sentence, use **aloud**.

Associate **allowed** with **allow** and **aloud** with **loud**.

Answers

1. *aloud*
2. *allowed*
3. *allowed*
4. *allowed*
5. *aloud*
6. *allowed*
7. *aloud*
8. *aloud*
9. *allowed*
10. *aloud*
11. *allowed*
12. *aloud*
13. *aloud*
14. *allowed*
15. *allowed*
16. *aloud*
17. *allowed*
18. *aloud*
19. *aloud*
20. *allowed*

ant – aunt *p. 47*

***Aunt** is on Spelling Plus list 50.*
Recommended for grade 5.

ant *n.* an insect
aunt *n.* sister of one's parent or wife of one's uncle

Once students know the difference between these words, they may not confuse them in their writing, despite the fact that they are pronounced alike by some speakers.

The word **aunt** is pronounced by some speakers with the **au** sound in **caught**. Students may pronounce it with this accent as an aid to spelling.

Point of interest: A dialectical variation of **ant** is **Emmet**, which survives as a surname.

Answers

1. *aunt*
2. *ant*
3. *ant*
4. *aunt*
5. *ant*
6. *ant*
7. *aunt*
8. *ant*
9. *aunt*
10. *aunt*
11. *ant*
12. *aunt*
13. *ant*
14. *ant*
15. *ant*
16. *aunt*
17. *aunt*
18. *ant*
19. *aunt*
20. *aunt*

are – our *p. 48*

***Are** is on Spelling Plus list 6.*
***Our** is on Spelling Plus list 8.*
Recommended for grade 1.

are *v.* a form of *to be,* as in, "They are here."
our *adj.* belonging to us

Technically, these words do not have the same pronunciation, but students may not be able to clearly hear the difference. Both words are used frequently by students throughout the grades.

Have students clearly pronounce **our** with the **ou** in **out** as they write it. Pronounce **are** like the letter **r**.

Answers

1. *our*
2. *are*
3. *our*
4. *our*
5. *are*
6. *are*
7. *our*
8. *are*
9. *are*
10. *are*
11. *our*
12. *our*
13. *are*
14. *our*
15. *are*
16. *are*
17. *our*
18. *our*
19. *our*
20. *are*

ate – eight *p. 49*

***Ate** is on Spelling Plus list 11.*
***Eight** is on Spelling Plus list 62.*
Recommended for grade 4.

ate *v.* consumed food, past tense of *to eat*
eight *n. adj.* the number 8

Both of these words are used with about the same frequency.

Ate has the same three letters as **eat** but the **e** is at the end rather than the beginning in **ate**.

The **gh** in **eight** was once pronounced with a guttural sound which no longer exists in English. The printed **g** in **eight** looks something like an 8.

Answers

1. *ate*
2. *eight*
3. *ate*
4. *ate*
5. *eight*
6. *eight*
7. *ate*
8. *eight*
9. *eight*
10. *ate*
11. *eight*
12. *ate*
13. *ate*
14. *eight*
15. *ate*
16. *eight*
17. *ate*
18. *ate*
19. *ate*
20. *eight*

be – bee *p. 50*

***Be** is on Spelling Plus list 10.*
Recommended for grade 1.

be *v.* to exist
bee *n.* a buzzing insect

Be is one of the most frequently used words in English. **Bee** is very infrequently used. Because of this, there is no need to teach this set unless students demonstrate confusion in their writing.

Bee comes from an Old English base meaning "tremble, quiver." How does this apply to the insect called a **bee**? How might this apply to a spelling bee or a quilting bee?

Answers

1. *bee*
2. *be*
3. *be*
4. *bee*
5. *bee*
6. *be*
7. *be*
8. *be*
9. *bee*
10. *be*
11. *be*
12. *be*
13. *bee*
14. *bee*
15. *be*
16. *be*
17. *bee*
18. *be*
19. *be*
20. *be*

bear – bare *p. 51*

***Bear** is on Spelling Plus list 30.*
Recommended for grade 3.

bear *n.* a large animal
v. to carry, put up with, stand
bare *adj.* without covering

Bear is much more frequently used as a verb than as a noun. **Bare** and the noun **bear** are used with about the same frequency.

Answers

1. *bare*
2. *bear*
3. *bear*
4. *bare*
5. *bear*
6. *bare*
7. *bear*
8. *bear*
9. *bear*
10. *bare*
11. *bare*
12. *bear*
13. *bare*
14. *bear*
15. *bear*
16. *bare*
17. *bear*
18. *bare*
19. *bear*
20. *bear*

beat – beet *p. 52*

Not on the Spelling Plus list.
Recommended for grade 3.

beat *v.* to hit again and again, or to win victory over
n. any of a series of movements or sounds, the beat of music
beet *n.* a vegetable

The verb **beat** is more frequently used than the noun. **Beet** is very infrequently used. This set need not be taught unless students show evidence of confusion in their writing.

Answers

1. *beat*
2. *beat*
3. *beat*
4. *beet*
5. *beat*
6. *beet*
7. *beet*
8. *beat*
9. *beet*
10. *beat*
11. *beat*
12. *beet*
13. *beet*
14. *beat*
15. *beet*
16. *beat*
17. *beat*
18. *beat*
19. *beet*
20. *beet*

berry – bury *p. 53*

Not on the Spelling Plus list.
Recommended for grade 4.

berry *n.* an edible fruit
bury *v.* to hide beneath the earth

Berry comes from Old English **berie.** **Bury** is from Old English **byrgan** and was spelled several ways in Middle English due to the variety of dialects. We use the western English spelling **bury** but the Kentish pronunciation **berry**.

Overpronounce **bury** to rhyme with **furry** as an aid to spelling.

Answers

1. *bury*
2. *bury*
3. *berry*
4. *berry*
5. *bury*
6. *berry*
7. *bury*
8. *berry*
9. *berry*
10. *berry*
11. *bury*
12. *bury*
13. *bury*
14. *berry*
15. *berry*
16. *bury*
17. *berry*
18. *berry*
19. *berry*
20. *bury*

blew – blue *p. 54*

***Blew** is on Spelling Plus list 33.*
***Blue** is on Spelling Plus list 18.*
Recommended for grade 3.

blew *v.* moved a current of air; did blow
blue *adj.* having the color blue
n. a color

Blue is used more often than **blew.**

Blew is the past tense of **blow.** There is only one letter difference between the two words. There are a number of words which form the past tense in this way, including **grow – grew**, **throw – threw.**

Blue came into English from Old French, where it was spelled **bleu.** It was sometimes spelled **blew** in Middle England.

Answers

1. *blue*
2. *blew*
3. *blew*
4. *blue*
5. *blue*
6. *blue*
7. *blew*
8. *blue*
9. *blew*
10. *blew*
11. *blue*
12. *blue*
13. *blew*
14. *blew*
15. *blew*
16. *blue*
17. *blew*
18. *blue*
19. *blew*
20. *blue*

board – bored *p. 55*

***Board** is on Spelling Plus list 38.*
Recommended for grade 4.

board *n.* a flat piece of lumber
v. to cover with boards; to get on
bored *v.* filled with boredom

Board can be linked to **oar** with the mnemonic sentence, "They used the b**oar**d as an **oar**."

Bored is the past tense form of **bore**. Add **-s** to **bore** to form **bores** and drop the **e** and add **-ing** to form **boring**.

Answers
1. *bored*
2. *bored*
3. *board*
4. *bored*
5. *board*
6. *board*
7. *board*
8. *bored*
9. *board*
10. *bored*
11. *bored*
12. *board*
13. *bored*
14. *board*
15. *board*
16. *bored*
17. *bored*
18. *board*
19. *bored*
20. *board*

break – brake *p. 56*

***Break** is on Spelling Plus list 34.*
Recommended for grade 3.

break *v.* to split into pieces
n. a crack or broken place
brake *n.* something which slows or stops motion

Brake probably was once a specific use of the word **bridle**. A bridle was used to slow or stop a horse just as a brake is used to slow or stop a vehicle.

Answers
1. *break*
2. *brake*
3. *brake*
4. *brake*
5. *break*
6. *break*
7. *brake*
8. *break*
9. *break*
10. *brake*
11. *break*
12. *brake*
13. *break*
14. *break*
15. *brake*
16. *brake*
17. *break*
18. *break*
19. *break*
20. *brake*

buy – by *p. 57*

***Buy** is on Spelling Plus list 40.*
***By** is on Spelling Plus list 10.*
Recommended for grade 2.

buy *v.* to purchase with money
by *prep.* near or beside, before
adv. close at hand, near

By is from Old English **bi**. The preposition **by** is one of the most common words in English.

The current spelling of **buy** represents southern and western English, while the pronunciation is from midland and northern English. This is also the case with **build** and **busy**. The endings **-s** and **-ing** can be added to **buy** to form **buys** and **buying**.

Answers
1. *buy*
2. *by*
3. *buy*
4. *by*
5. *buy*
6. *buy*
7. *by*
8. *buy*
9. *buy*
10. *by*
11. *by*
12. *buy*
13. *by*
14. *buy*
15. *by*
16. *by*
17. *by*
18. *buy*
19. *by*
20. *by*

buy – by – bye *p. 58*

***Buy** is on Spelling Plus list 40.*
***By** is on Spelling Plus list 10.*
***Goodbye** is on Spelling Plus list 18.*
Recommended for grade 4.

buy *v.* to purchase with money
by *prep.* near or beside, before
adv. close at hand, near
bye *interj.* short for *goodbye*

See the previous lesson for information on the words **by** and **buy**.

Bye comes from **goodbye**, which comes from the old saying, "God be with ye." Later **good** was substituted for **God** after "good day" and "good night."

Answers
1. *buy*
2. *bye*
3. *by*
4. *bye bye*
5. *buy*
6. *by*
7. *bye*
8. *buy*
9. *bye*
10. *by*
11. *by*
12. *bye*
13. *by*
14. *by*
15. *bye*
16. *buy*
17. *bye*
18. *bye*
19. *buy*
20. *by*

capital – capitol *p. 59*

Not on the Spelling Plus list.
Recommended for grade 6.

capital *adj.* of most importance
n. city or town which is the seat of government
capitol *n.* the building in which Congress or a state legislature meets

Capital is from Old French, originally from the Latin root **caput**, meaning "head" and the suffix **-al**, meaning "pertaining to."

Capitol was a temple in ancient Rome dedicated to Jupiter. Remind students to capitalize this word only when it specifically refers to the Capitol building of the U.S., as it does once on this worksheet. Associate **capitol** with **building**. All other meanings have the spelling **capital**.

Answers

1. *capital*
2. *Capitol*
3. *capital*
4. *capital*
5. *capitol*
6. *capital*
7. *capitol*
8. *capital*
9. *capitol*
10. *capital*
11. *capital*
12. *capitol*
13. *capital*
14. *capital*
15. *capital*
16. *capitol*
17. *capital*
18. *capital*
19. *capital*
20. *capitol*

ceiling – sealing *p. 60*

Not on the Spelling Plus list.
Recommended for grade 6.

ceiling *n.* the inside top part of a room, opposite the floor
sealing *v.* closing, shutting, fastening

Ceiling had a large variety of spellings in early modern English, including **sylling**, **seeling**, **cieling**, and **seyling**. It comes from an Old French word meaning "to conceal."

The base word of **sealing** is **seal**. Add **-s** to **seal** to form **seals**, and add **-ed** to form **sealed**. A **seal** was originally a device with a design or lettering for stamping on paper, wax, or metal. Before envelopes with gummed flaps were invented, wax was used for sealing documents. It could be stamped with a unique seal to attest its authenticity. The word is related to the Latin word for **sign**.

Answers

1. *sealing*
2. *sealing*
3. *ceiling*
4. *sealing*
5. *ceiling*
6. *sealing*
7. *ceiling*
8. *ceiling*
9. *ceiling*
10. *sealing*
11. *sealing*
12. *ceiling*
13. *ceiling*
14. *sealing*
15. *ceiling*
16. *sealing*
17. *sealing*
18. *ceiling*
19. *sealing*
20. *ceiling*

celery – salary *p. 61*

Not on the Spelling Plus list.
Recommended for grade 5.

celery *n.* a vegetable
salary *n.* fixed pay for regular work

These words are not technically homophones, but the pronunciation is confusingly similar. **Salary** is more frequently used.

Both words come from Latin through French. The word **salary** is related to **salt**, and was originally money allowed to Roman soldiers for the purchase of salt. In ancient times, salt was a precious commodity, at times equal in value to gold. The first three letters of **salary** and **salt** are the same.

Answers

1. *celery*
2. *salary*
3. *celery*
4. *celery*
5. *salary*
6. *celery*
7. *salary*
8. *salary*
9. *salary*
10. *celery*
11. *salary*
12. *celery*
13. *celery*
14. *salary*
15. *celery*
16. *salary*
17. *salary*
18. *celery*
19. *salary*
20. *celery*

cell – sell *p. 62*

Not on the Spelling Plus list.
Recommended for grade 5.

cell *n.* a small room, such as in a prison, or the basic unit of life
sell *v.* to exchange something for money

The word **cell** comes from Latin through Old French and is related to a Latin word meaning "conceal." The original meaning was a small apartment. The meaning was expanded to include a compartment of a honeycomb, the cell of a plant, and later many other scientific uses.

Sell is from Old English. Associate **sell** with **sale**.

Answers

1. *sell*
2. *cell*
3. *cell*
4. *sell*
5. *sell*
6. *sell*
7. *cell*
8. *cell*
9. *sell*
10. *cell*
11. *sell*
12. *sell*
13. *cell*
14. *sell*
15. *cell*
16. *cell*
17. *cell*
18. *sell*
19. *sell*
20. *cell*

cent – sent *p. 63*

Not on the Spelling Plus list.
Recommended for grade 2.

cent *n.* a penny
sent *v.* to cause or direct to go away, did send

Both of these words are used with about equal frequency.

Cent comes from **per cent**, from Latin through French. **Per cent** (now generally written as one word, **percent**) means "per hundred." In the United States in 1786, the word **cent** was applied to a proposed coin worth 1/100 of the basic unit of money, the dollar.

Sent is the past tense of **send**. Other words which form the past tense this way include **bend – bent** and **lend – lent**.

Answers

1. *cent*
2. *sent*
3. *sent*
4. *cent*
5. *sent*
6. *cent*
7. *sent*
8. *cent*
9. *sent*
10. *sent*
11. *cent*
12. *sent*
13. *cent*
14. *cent*
15. *cent*
16. *sent*
17. *sent*
18. *cent*
19. *sent*
20. *sent*

cent – sent – scent *p. 64*

Not on the Spelling Plus list.
Recommended for grade 6.

cent *n.* a penny
sent *v.* to cause or direct to go away, did send
scent *n.* a smell
v. to smell or to track by smell

Both **cent** and **sent** are used frequently in English. **Scent** is very infrequently used.

Cent comes from **per cent**, from Latin through French. See more about this word in the previous lesson.

Sent is the past tense of **send**.

Scent comes from an Old French word meaning "to feel, sense, perceive, smell." The unexplained spelling first appeared in the 1700's.

Answers

1. *scent*
2. *sent*
3. *sent*
4. *cent*
5. *scent*
6. *sent*
7. *cent*
8. *scent*
9. *sent*
10. *cent*
11. *sent*
12. *scent*
13. *sent*
14. *cent*
15. *scent*
16. *cent*
17. *sent*
18. *scent*
19. *sent*
20. *cent*

cereal – serial *p. 65*

Not on the Spelling Plus list.
Recommended for grade 6.

cereal *n.* edible grain, breakfast food made from grain
serial *n. adj.* forming a series

Neither of these words is frequently used in English.

The word **cereal** comes from **Ceres**, the goddess of grain, the harvest, and agriculture in Roman mythology. There was a festival called Cerealia each April which honored Ceres.

Serial comes from **series**, meaning "row, chain" and the suffix **-al**, meaning "pertaining to." Associate **serial** with **series**.

Answers

1. *cereal*
2. *cereal*
3. *serial*
4. *serial*
5. *cereal*
6. *serial*
7. *serial*
8. *cereal*
9. *cereal*
10. *serial*
11. *cereal*
12. *serial*
13. *cereal*
14. *cereal*
15. *serial*
16. *serial*
17. *cereal*
18. *serial*
19. *cereal*
20. *cereal*

chews – choose *p. 66*

***Choose** is on Spelling Plus list 30.*
Recommended for grade 3.

chews *v.* crushes or grinds with the teeth, does chew
choose *v.* to select

Choose is the more frequently used word in this pair. Both words are from Old English.

Chews is the base word **chew** plus the ending **-s**. Add **-ed** to form **chewed** and **-ing** to form **chewing**.

Choose was generally spelled **chuse** from the 1600's to the 1800's. Samuel Johnson established the spelling **choose** in the first English dictionary. The endings **-s** and **-ing** can be added to this base word to form **chooses** and **choosing**.

Answers

1. *choose*
2. *chews*
3. *chews*
4. *choose*
5. *chews*
6. *choose*
7. *choose*
8. *chews*
9. *choose*
10. *chews*
11. *chews*
12. *chews*
13. *choose*
14. *choose*
15. *chews*
16. *choose*
17. *chews*
18. *choose*
19. *chews*
20. *choose*

clothes – close *p. 67*

Clothes *is on Spelling Plus list 49.*
Close *is on Spelling Plus list 14.*
Recommended for grade 5.

clothes *n.* clothing
close *v.* to shut

Both of these words are frequently used in English.

Clothes comes from **cloth** + **-es**. Clothes are made from more than one piece of cloth. In Middle England, this word was sometimes spelled **cloaths** or **close**.

Close comes from Latin through Old French. The first meaning was "enclosure, cloister." It later came to be used as a verb and is now only infrequently used as a noun. **Close** can also be pronounced with a soft **s** as an adjective or adverb meaning "nearby."

Answers

1. *clothes*
2. *close*
3. *close*
4. *clothes*
5. *close*
6. *clothes*
7. *clothes*
8. *close*
9. *clothes*
10. *close*
11. *clothes*
12. *clothes*
13. *clothes*
14. *close*
15. *close*
16. *close*
17. *clothes*
18. *close*
19. *close*
20. *clothes*

conscience – conscious *p. 68*

Spelling Plus list 69.
Recommended for grade 6.

conscience *n.* inner sense of right and wrong
conscious *adj.* aware; in a normal waking state

Both of these words ultimately come from the same Latin source, **con**-, meaning "with", and **sci** meaning "know." Although the pronunciation is not identical, it is confusingly similar. The word **conscious** is somewhat more frequently used.

Associate **conscience** with **science** and overpronounce it as **con – science** when spelling. Associate **conscious** with **unconscious**.

Answers

1. *conscious*
2. *conscience*
3. *conscious*
4. *conscience*
5. *conscious*
6. *conscience*
7. *conscious*
8. *conscious*
9. *conscience*
10. *conscience*
11. *conscious*
12. *conscious*
13. *conscious*
14. *conscience*
15. *conscious*
16. *conscience*
17. *conscious*
18. *conscience*
19. *conscience*
20. *conscience*

council – counsel *p. 69*

Not on the Spelling Plus list.
Recommended for grade 6.

council *n.* a group of people called together for a special reason
counsel *v.* to advise, give advice to *n.* advice

At one time in English, these words were blended, although they came from somewhat different Latin roots, through French. The differentiation began in the 1600's. **Council** is used more frequently than **counsel**.

Council comes from **con** meaning "together" and **calare** meaning "call." A council is called together.

Counsel is related to the word **consult**. A **counselor** is someone with whom you **consult** for information and advice.

Answers

1. *counsel*
2. *council*
3. *council*
4. *counsel*
5. *council*
6. *counsel*
7. *counsel*
8. *counsel*
9. *council*
10. *council*
11. *counsel*
12. *council*
13. *counsel*
14. *counsel*
15. *council*
16. *counsel*
17. *council*
18. *council*
19. *counsel*
20. *council*

course – coarse *p. 70*

Course *is on Spelling Plus list 42.*
Recommended for grade 4.

course *n.* progress from one point to the next, a class or unit of instruction leading to a degree
coarse *adj.* rough

Course is used *much* more frequently than **coarse** in English. **Coarse** has a very limited meaning and synonyms are more frequently used to express that meaning.

Course comes from Latin through Old French. The stem **curs** meant "run," and is the stem for **cursive**, handwriting which runs together.

Coarse is of unknown origin, and has been spelled **cors**, **corse**, and **course**. If the word **rough** makes sense in the sentence, use **coarse**.

Answers

1. *course*
2. *coarse*
3. *coarse*
4. *course*
5. *course*
6. *coarse*
7. *course*
8. *coarse*
9. *course*
10. *coarse*
11. *course*
12. *coarse*
13. *course*
14. *course*
15. *coarse*
16. *coarse*
17. *course*
18. *course*
19. *coarse*
20. *course*

creak – creek *p. 71*

Not on the Spelling Plus list.
Recommended for grade 3.

creak *v.* to make a harsh, shrill, grating sound
n. such a sound
creek *n.* a small stream

Neither of these words is frequently used.

Creak was originally a synonym of **croak**. Eventually **creak** came to be a *high-pitched* grating sound and **croak** came to be a *low-pitched* grating sound. Link the two words as an aid to spelling.

Creek was first a narrow inlet in a coast. It later came to mean an arm or branch of a river, somewhat larger than a brook. Both **brook** and **creek** have double vowels.

Answers

1. *creek*
2. *creek*
3. *creak*
4. *creak*
5. *creak*
6. *creek*
7. *creak*
8. *creek*
9. *creek*
10. *creak*
11. *creek*
12. *creek*
13. *creek*
14. *creak*
15. *creak*
16. *creek*
17. *creak*
18. *creek*
19. *creak*
20. *creak*

dear – deer *p. 72*

***Dear** is on Spelling Plus list 26.*
Recommended for grade 3.

dear *adj.* beloved, highly thought of
deer *n.* an animal

Dear is much more frequently used than **deer**. The meanings are quite different. The word **deer** can be either singular or plural.

Remind students to capitalize **Dear** at the beginning of a letter and at the beginning of a quote. It must be capitalized four times in the worksheet.

Answers

1. *deer*
2. *Dear*
3. *dear*
4. *deer*
5. *dear*
6. *dear*
7. *Dear*
8. *deer*
9. *deer*
10. *dear*
11. *Dear*
12. *deer*
13. *deer*
14. *dear*
15. *deer*
16. *Dear*
17. *dear*
18. *deer*
19. *deer*
20. *deer*

desert – dessert *p. 73*

Not on the Spelling Plus list.
Recommended for grade 5.

desert *n.* a waste tract of country, generally dry and with little vegetation
v. to forsake, abandon, make waste
dessert *n.* a sweet course at the end of a meal

The verb **desert** has the same pronunciation as **dessert**. In contrast, the noun **desert** is accented on the first syllable.

Note that the sense meaning of **desert** is "waste."

The double **s** in **dessert** can be remembered with the mnemonic sentence, "Dessert is **s**o **s**weet."

Answers

1. *dessert*
2. *desert*
3. *dessert*
4. *desert*
5. *desert*
6. *dessert*
7. *desert*
8. *dessert*
9. *dessert*
10. *desert*
11. *desert*
12. *dessert*
13. *desert*
14. *dessert*
15. *dessert*
16. *desert*
17. *desert*
18. *dessert*
19. *dessert*
20. *desert*

dew – do – due *p. 74*

***Do** is on Spelling Plus list 10.*
Recommended for grade 4.

dew *n.* moisture in small drops
do *v.* to carry out, finish
due *adj.* owed and payable

Do is by far the most frequently used of these words. Students are unlikely to confuse these until they begin using **dew** or **due** in their writing. There is no need to introduce this set until some confusion is evident.

Due comes from Old French and is from **de-** meaning "away" and **habere** meaning "have." It means to have something away from someone, to have or hold what belongs to another.

Due may also be an adverb, as in, "The ship sailed due west."

Answers

1. *do*
2. *do*
3. *dew*
4. *do*
5. *due*
6. *dew*
7. *do*
8. *due*
9. *do*
10. *due*
11. *dew*
12. *do*
13. *due*
14. *do*
15. *dew*
16. *do*
17. *due*
18. *dew*
19. *do*
20. *due*

die – dye *p. 75*

***Die** is on Spelling Plus list 33.*
Recommended for grade 3.

die *v.* to stop living
dye *n.* a chemical used to change the color of something
v. to change the color of something using dye

Die is by far the more frequently used of these two words. Samuel Johnson had both words spelled as **die** in his first English dictionary. Joseph Addison, a popular author of the time, had both words spelled as **dye**. Long ago, **y** was used more frequently than **i**.

Answers

1. *die*
2. *die*
3. *dye*
4. *die*
5. *dye*
6. *die*
7. *dye*
8. *dye*
9. *dye*
10. *die*
11. *die*
12. *dye*
13. *dye*
14. *die*
15. *dye*
16. *die*
17. *die*
18. *dye*
19. *dye*
20. *die*

fair – fare *p. 76*

***Fair** is on Spelling Plus list 32.*
Recommended for grade 3.

fair *adj.* just and honest
n. a festival or carnival
fare *n.* money paid for passage on a bus or train, or a passenger who pays a fare

The adjective **fair**, meaning just and honest, comes from Old English **faeger**. The noun **fair**, meaning a festival, comes from Old French **feire**. These words are homonyms.

Fair is much more frequently used than **fare**.

Answers

1. *fare*
2. *fair*
3. *fair*
4. *fare*
5. *fair*
6. *fair*
7. *fare*
8. *fair*
9. *fare*
10. *fare*
11. *fair*
12. *fair*
13. *fare*
14. *fare*
15. *fair*
16. *fair*
17. *fair*
18. *fare*
19. *fair*
20. *fare*

fir – fur *p. 77*

Not on the Spelling Plus list.
Recommended for grade 3.

fir *n.* a kind of tree; wood from that tree
fur *n.* soft, thick animal hair

Neither of these words is frequently used. Introduce this pair when and if students show confusion in their writing.

Answers

1. *fur*
2. *fir*
3. *fir*
4. *fur*
5. *fir*
6. *fir*
7. *fur*
8. *fur*
9. *fir*
10. *fur*
11. *fur*
12. *fur*
13. *fir*
14. *fur*
15. *fur*
16. *fir*
17. *fir*
18. *fur*
19. *fur*
20. *fur*

flew – flu *p. 78*

Not on the Spelling Plus list.
Recommended for grade 3.

flew *v.* moved through the air, did fly
flu *n.* a sickness, short for *influenza*

Flew is more common than **flu**.

The past tense of **fly** in Middle English was **flow**. The current past tense, **flew**, is unexplained. Similar past tense forms include **blow** – **blew** and **grow** – **grew**.

Flu is a short form of **influenza**. A 1743 epidemic in Rome was named influenza, a word that comes from a Latin root meaning "to flow."

Flue, a pipe through which smoke, hot air, or gas passes, is also a homophone. It is rarely used.

Answers

1. *flu*
2. *flew*
3. *flew*
4. *flu*
5. *flew*
6. *flu*
7. *flew*
8. *flu*
9. *flu*
10. *flew*
11. *flew*
12. *flew*
13. *flu*
14. *flew*
15. *flew*
16. *flu*
17. *flu*
18. *flew*
19. *flew*
20. *flu*

flour – flower *p. 79*

Not on the Spelling Plus list.
Recommended for grade 4.

flour *n.* a fine powdery substance usually made by grinding grain
flower *n.* a blossom or bloom

Flower is used more frequently than **flour**.

These homophones were once a single word which was variously spelled **flower**, **flur**, or **flour** in Middle England. The only spelling recorded by Samuel Johnson in his first English dictionary was **flower**, and it continued to be the spelling for both meanings until the early 1900's.

Answers

1. *flower*
2. *flour*
3. *flower*
4. *flower*
5. *flower*
6. *flour*
7. *flour*
8. *flower*
9. *flour*
10. *flour*
11. *flower*
12. *flower*
13. *flour*
14. *flower*
15. *flour*
16. *flour*
17. *flour*
18. *flower*
19. *flower*
20. *flour*

for – four *p. 80*

***For** is on Spelling Plus list 17.*
***Four** is on Spelling Plus list 21.*
Recommended for grade 2.

for *prep.* with the purpose of
four *n. adj.* the number 4

Both of these words are frequently used. **For** is one of the most common words in English.

Both words come from Old English. **Four** was pronounced **feower** in Old English.

For can also be used as a subordinating conjunction, as in, "We can't go now, for it is dark."

Answers

1. *four*
2. *for*
3. *four*
4. *for*
5. *for*
6. *for*
7. *four*
8. *for*
9. *four*
10. *for*
11. *for*
12. *four*
13. *four*
14. *for*
15. *for*
16. *for*
17. *four*
18. *for*
19. *four*
20. *for*

form – from *p. 81*

***From** is on Spelling Plus list 20.*
Recommended for grade 4.

form *n.* the arrangement of parts of a thing
v. to make or give shape to
from *prep.* source or beginning of ideas or action

These words have quite different pronunciations, but are often confused because of the similarity in spelling. Both are frequently used, but **from** is one of the most used words in English.

Careful pronunciation will help with spelling.

Answers

1. *from*
2. *from*
3. *form*
4. *from*
5. *form*
6. *form*
7. *from*
8. *form*
9. *from*
10. *from*
11. *form*
12. *form*
13. *from*
14. *form*
15. *from*
16. *form*
17. *form*
18. *from*
19. *form*
20. *from*

forth – fourth *p. 82*

***Fourth** is on Spelling Plus List 42.*
Recommended for grade 4.

forth *adv.* forward
fourth *adj. n.* the one after third, the 4th

Children are likely to use **fourth** more often than **forth**.

Associate **forth** with **forward**. Both have the same first three letters.

Associate **fourth** with **four**, its root.

Answers

1. *fourth*
2. *forth*
3. *forth*
4. *fourth*
5. *fourth*
6. *forth*
7. *forth*
8. *fourth*
9. *fourth*
10. *fourth*
11. *forth*
12. *fourth*
13. *fourth*
14. *fourth*
15. *forth*
16. *fourth*
17. *forth*
18. *fourth*
19. *fourth*
20. *fourth*

great – grate *p. 83*

***Great** is on Spelling Plus list 34.*
Recommended for grade 3.

great *adj.* remarkable, better than good
grate *v.* to grind into shreds, often with a harsh, scraping sound
n. a heavy metal framework used to cover a hole

Great is by far the more frequently used of these two words.

Great was originally pronounced **gret**, with the more regular sound for **ea** as in **head**. A mnemonic sentence is, "This is gr**eat** to **eat**."

Grate was originally a noun and only later came to be a verb.

Answers

1. *great*
2. *grate*
3. *great*
4. *great*
5. *grate*
6. *great*
7. *grate*
8. *great*
9. *great*
10. *grate*
11. *great*
12. *great*
13. *great*
14. *grate*
15. *great*
16. *great*
17. *great*
18. *grate*
19. *great*
20. *grate*

groan – grown *p. 84*

Not on the Spelling Plus list.
Recommended for grade 3.

groan *v.* to make a deep sound of pain
n. a groaning sound
grown *adj.* fully developed, mature
v. increased in size, became

Grown is used more frequently than **groan**.

Groan is related to **grin**, which originally meant to draw back the lips and show the teeth in pain or anger.

Grown comes from **grow**, which is related to the words **green** and **grass**. Some other words which are conjugated the same way include:
blow – blew – blown
know – knew – known
throw – threw – thrown

Answers

1. *grown*
2. *grown*
3. *groan*
4. *grown*
5. *groan*
6. *grown*
7. *groan*
8. *groan*
9. *groan*
10. *grown*
11. *grown*
12. *groan*
13. *grown*
14. *grown*
15. *grown*
16. *groan*
17. *groan*
18. *grown*
19. *groan*
20. *groan*

guessed – guest *p. 85*

***Guess** is on Spelling Plus list 56.*
Recommended for grade 5.

guessed *v.* supposed, did guess
guest *n.* a visitor

Both of these words are used with about the same frequency.

Guessed is **guess** plus the inflectional ending -**ed**. The endings -**es** and -**ing** can be added to the base word to form **guesses** and **guessing**. **Guess** originally meant "take aim." It came to mean "form an estimate or approximate judgment of." The spelling with **gu** dates from the 1600's, when the word was pronounced with a guttural or stopped **g**. This sound could also be spelled with **gh**.

Guest is from Old French. It was spelled **gest** in Middle England.

Answers

1. *guessed*
2. *guessed*
3. *guest*
4. *guest*
5. *guest*
6. *guessed*
7. *guest*
8. *guessed*
9. *guessed*
10. *guest*
11. *guessed*
12. *guessed*
13. *guest*
14. *guest*
15. *guessed*
16. *guessed*
17. *guest*
18. *guest*
19. *guessed*
20. *guest*

hair – hare *p. 86*

***Hair** is on Spelling Plus list 32.*
Recommended for grade 3.

hair *n.* the covering on a person's head and on the bodies of mammals
hare *n.* an animal similar to a rabbit

Hair is *much* more frequently used than **hare**. Unless students confuse the words, there is no need to introduce them.

The present spelling and pronunciation of **hair** is abnormal. The word used to be pronounced like **here**.

Imagine **air** blowing through your **hair**.

Answers

1. *hair*
2. *hair*
3. *hare*
4. *hair*
5. *hair*
6. *hair*
7. *hare*
8. *hare*
9. *hair*
10. *hare*
11. *hair*
12. *hair*
13. *hare*
14. *hair*
15. *hair*
16. *hare*
17. *hare*
18. *hair*
19. *hare*
20. *hair*

hall – haul *p. 87*

Not on the Spelling Plus list.
Recommended for grade 4.

hall *n.* a passageway or corridor; a large central room
haul *v.* to carry

Hall is more common than **haul**.

Hall originally meant a spacious, roofed place. It comes from a root meaning "to cover" which is also the root for the word **hell**, as well as **ceiling**, **cell**, and **conceal** (through Latin).

The earliest form of **haul** was **hall**, a variation of the archaic word **hale** which meant "draw, pull."

Associate **hall** with **wall**. A **hall** has a **wall**.

Answers

1. *hall*
2. *haul*
3. *hall*
4. *hall*
5. *haul*
6. *hall*
7. *hall*
8. *haul*
9. *haul*
10. *hall*
11. *haul*
12. *hall*
13. *haul*
14. *haul*
15. *haul*
16. *hall*
17. *hall*
18. *haul*
19. *hall*
20. *haul*

hay – hey *p. 88*

Not on the Spelling Plus list.
Recommended for grade 4.

hay *n.* cut and dried grass used to feed animals
hey *interj.* an expression used to attract attention

Neither of these words is very frequently used.

The word **hey** is generally used at the beginning of a sentence and is therefore usually capitalized. Capitalize any word which begins a sentence.

Answers

1. *hay*
2. *Hey*
3. *hay*
4. *Hey*
5. *Hey*
6. *hay*
7. *Hey*
8. *hay*
9. *hay*
10. *Hey*
11. *hay*
12. *Hey*
13. *hay*
14. *hay*
15. *Hay*
16. *Hey*
17. *hay*
18. *hay*
19. *Hey*
20. *Hey*

heal – heel *p. 89*

Not on the Spelling Plus list.
Recommended for grade 3.

heal *v.* to make well or healthy
heel *n.* the back part of the foot, the part of a stocking or shoe near one's heel

Heel is somewhat more frequently used than **heal**.

Heal comes from the same root as **whole** and has the sense of "making whole." Link it with **health**.

Heel can be linked with **feel**. You can **feel** your **heel**.

Answers

1. *heal*
2. *heel*
3. *heal*
4. *heal*
5. *heel*
6. *heal*
7. *heal*
8. *heal*
9. *heel*
10. *heel*
11. *heel*
12. *heal*
13. *heel*
14. *heal*
15. *heel*
16. *heal*
17. *heal*
18. *heel*
19. *heel*
20. *heal*

hear – here *p. 90*

***Hear** is on Spelling Plus list 26.*
***Here** is on Spelling Plus list 13.*
Recommended for grade 3.

hear *v.* to sense sounds with the ear
here *adv.* at or in this place

Here is used somewhat more frequently than **hear**, although both are quite common.

Link **hear** with **ear**. You **hear** with your **ear**.

Link **here** with **there** and **where**. All of these words refer to *place*.

Answers

1. *hear*
2. *hear*
3. *here*
4. *hear*
5. *here*
6. *here*
7. *here*
8. *hear*
9. *here*
10. *hear*
11. *hear*
12. *hear*
13. *here*
14. *hear*
15. *here*
16. *here*
17. *here*
18. *hear*
19. *here*
20. *here*

heard – herd *p. 91*

***Heard** is on Spelling Plus list 39.*
Recommended for grade 4.

heard *v.* sensed sounds with the ear, did hear
herd *n.* a group of animals
v. to gather or drive animals in a group

Heard is much more frequently used than **herd**.

Heard is the past tense of the word **hear**. It was once pronounced like the word **hard**. Link it with **ear**. He **heard** with his **ear**.

Answers

1. *herd*
2. *heard*
3. *heard*
4. *heard*
5. *herd*
6. *heard*
7. *herd*
8. *heard*
9. *heard*
10. *herd*
11. *herd*
12. *heard*
13. *herd*
14. *heard*
15. *herd*
16. *heard*
17. *heard*
18. *herd*
19. *herd*
20. *heard*

higher – hire *p. 92*

***High** is on Spelling Plus list 40.*
Recommended for grade 4.

higher *adj. adv.* taller, more high
hire *v.* to take on an employee

Higher is more frequently used than **hire**, although both are common.

Higher is **high** plus the ending -**er**, making it a comparative adjective. The ending -**est** can also be added to **high** to form a superlative adjective, **highest**. The word **high** was once pronounced like **hee**. The long **e** was raised to a long **i** as in **die** during the Great Vowel Shift between 1400 and 1600 A.D. Pronunciations of a large number of words changed at that time.

Answers

1. *hire*
2. *higher*
3. *hire*
4. *hire*
5. *higher*
6. *higher*
7. *higher*
8. *hire*
9. *hire*
10. *higher*
11. *hire*
12. *higher*
13. *higher*
14. *hire*
15. *higher, higher*
16. *hire*
17. *higher*
18. *higher*
19. *hire*
20. *higher*

hole – whole *p. 93*

***Whole** is on Spelling Plus list 23.*
Recommended for grade 2.

hole *n.* a hollowed out place, an opening or break in something
whole *adj.* complete

Whole is more frequently used than **hole**, although both are common.

Hole comes from a root meaning "cover." Words such as **hall**, **hell**, and **hollow** also come from that root, as do words from Latin including **cell**, **ceiling**, and **conceal**.

Whole was spelled **hol** in Old English. The spelling with a **w** corresponded to a widespread dialectical pronunciation with **w** in the 1600's. The spelling changed permanently but the pronunciation did not. The **w** can be sounded as an aid to spelling.

Answers

1. *whole*
2. *whole*
3. *hole*
4. *whole*
5. *hole*
6. *whole*
7. *hole*
8. *hole*
9. *hole*
10. *whole*
11. *whole*
12. *whole*
13. *hole*
14. *whole*
15. *hole*
16. *whole*
17. *hole*
18. *hole*
19. *hole*
20. *whole*

horse – hoarse *p. 94*

***Horse** is on Spelling Plus list 17.*
Recommended for grade 5.

horse *n.* a large animal which can be ridden
hoarse *adj.* rough and deep-sounding

Horse is much more frequently used than **hoarse**.

Horse was spelled **hors** in Old English. Originally the word could be either singular or plural, like **deer** or **sheep**. The plural **horses** appears in the early 1300's.

Hoarse and **coarse** can be linked. Both have the sense of "rough."

Answers

1. *horse*
2. *hoarse*
3. *hoarse*
4. *hoarse*
5. *horse*
6. *horse*
7. *hoarse*
8. *horse*
9. *horse*
10. *horse*
11. *hoarse*
12. *horse*
13. *hoarse*
14. *hoarse*
15. *horse*
16. *hoarse*
17. *horse*
18. *horse*
19. *hoarse*
20. *hoarse*

hour – our *p. 95*

***Hour** is on Spelling Plus list 17.*
***Our** is on Spelling Plus list 8.*
Recommended for grade 2.

hour *n.* 60 minutes
our *adj.* belonging to us

Both of these words are very frequently used in English.

The word **hour** was spelled **ure** or **our** in Middle English. The **h** was added to reflect the word's Latin roots. An **h** was added for the same reason to **humble**, **herb**, and **humor**. It influenced the pronunciation of those words but not of **hour**. As long as students know the correct pronunciation of the word, they can overpronounce it as an aid to spelling, giving the **h** a sound.

Answers

1. *hour*
2. *our*
3. *hour*
4. *hour*
5. *our*
6. *our*
7. *our*
8. *hour*
9. *our*
10. *hour*
11. *our*
12. *our*
13. *hour*
14. *our*
15. *hour*
16. *hour*
17. *hour*
18. *our*
19. *our*
20. *hour*

I – eye *p. 96*

***I** is on Spelling Plus list 2.*
***Eye** is on Spelling Plus list 30.*
Recommended for grade 3.

I *pron.* the person speaking
eye *n.* the organ of sight

The word **I** is one of the most frequently used words in English.

In Old English, **ic** was used instead of **I** to refer to oneself. Around 1200, the reduced form **i** was used when the word was in a stressed position. Finally **i** came to be generalized to all positions, although some dialects of English still use **ich**. Now, the word **I** must always be capitalized. This began when manuscripts were handwritten. The small **i** was likely to be lost or attached to another word. A capital **I** helped keep it a distinct and separate word.

Answers

1. *eye*
2. *I*
3. *I*
4. *I*
5. *eye*
6. *I*
7. *eye*
8. *I*
9. *eye*
10. *eye*
11. *eye*
12. *I*
13. *I*
14. *eye*
15. *I*
16. *I*
17. *eye*
18. *I*
19. *eye*
20. *eye*

its – it's *p. 97*

Spelling Plus list 22.
Recommended for grade 2.

its *adj.* belonging to it
it's contraction for *it is* or *it has*

These words are *very* common and very frequently confused. An **'s** is added to nouns to show possession, but there is currently no apostrophe in the possessive **its**. This word *did* have an apostrophe until the early 1800's.

It is is contracted, or shortened, by removing the **i** in **is**, replacing it with an apostrophe, and contracting the two words into one word, **it's**. If "it is" can be substituted in the sentence, use **it's**.

Remind students to capitalize words at the beginning of a sentence.

Answers

1. *it's*
2. *its*
3. *Its*
4. *It's*
5. *its*
6. *It's*
7. *it's*
8. *Its*
9. *it's*
10. *it's*
11. *its*
12. *It's*
13. *its*
14. *it's*
15. *It's*
16. *Its*
17. *it's*
18. *Its*
19. *it's*
20. *Its*

lead – led *p. 98*

***Lead** is on Spelling Plus list 28.*
***Led** is on Spelling Plus list 5.*
Recommended for grade 3.

lead *n.* a heavy, bluish-gray metal
led *v.* guided, did lead

Led is more common than its homophone **lead**.

Lead can be pronounced with a short **e** as in the noun **lead**, or with a long **e** as in the verb **to lead**. Since **led** is the past tense form of **to lead**, students may have a great deal of difficulty with these two words, especially since **read** and its past tense **read** are spelled identically but have the same pronunciations as **lead – led**.

Answers

1. *led*
2. *lead*
3. *lead*
4. *lead*
5. *led*
6. *lead*
7. *led*
8. *led*
9. *lead*
10. *led*
11. *lead*
12. *lead*
13. *led*
14. *led*
15. *lead*
16. *lead*
17. *led*
18. *led*
19. *led*
20. *lead*

loose – lose *p. 99*

***Loose** is on Spelling Plus list 30.*
***Lose** is on Spelling Plus list 23.*
Recommended for grade 3.

loose *adj.* free, unattached, not connected or bound
lose *v.* to misplace, suffer the loss of

These words do not have the same pronunciation, but are frequently confused in writing as well as in reading. **Lose** is more common.

Loose rhymes with other words spelled in this pattern, including **goose** and **noose** (not **choose**).

Lose was once pronounced with a long **o** as in **chose** and **rose**. The change in pronunciation is thought to have been influenced by the pronunciation of **loose**. A mnemonic is, "If you use just one **o**, you l**o**se."

Answers

1. *loose*
2. *lose*
3. *lose*
4. *loose*
5. *loose*
6. *lose*
7. *loose*
8. *loose*
9. *lose*
10. *lose*
11. *lose*
12. *loose*
13. *loose*
14. *lose*
15. *loose*
16. *lose*
17. *lose*
18. *loose*
19. *lose*
20. *loose*

maid – made *p. 100*

***Made** is on Spelling Plus list 11.*
Recommended for grade 3.

maid *n.* a girl or female servant
made *v.* did make

Made is used much more often than **maid**.

Maid is a shortening of the word **maiden**, which originally meant a young, unmarried girl.

Made is the past tense form of **make**. There is only one letter difference between **make** and **made**.

Answers

1. *made*
2. *made*
3. *maid*
4. *made*
5. *maid*
6. *made*
7. *maid*
8. *made*
9. *made*
10. *maid*
11. *maid*
12. *made*
13. *made*
14. *made*
15. *maid*
16. *made*
17. *maid*
18. *made*
19. *made*
20. *maid*

mail – male *p. 101*

Not on the Spelling Plus list.
Recommended for grade 3.

mail *n.* letters and packages handled by the Post Office
v. to send by mail
male *n. adj.* opposite of female

Both of these words are used with about equal frequency.

Mail came through Old French from a German word which meant "a traveling bag, wallet." It came to mean items handled by the postal system and in the 1900's began to be used as a verb meaning to put such items in a postbox. A rare homonym, **mail**, refers to a flexible body armor, a coat of mail.

Male comes from the same Latin root as **masculine**.

Answers

1. *male*
2. *mail*
3. *mail*
4. *male*
5. *mail*
6. *mail*
7. *mail*
8. *male*
9. *male*
10. *mail*
11. *male*
12. *male*
13. *male*
14. *mail*
15. *mail*
16. *male*
17. *mail*
18. *mail*
19. *male*
20. *mail*

main – mane *p. 102*

***Main** is on Spelling Plus list 32.*
Recommended for grade 3.

main *adj.* most important
mane *n.* the long heavy hair on the neck of some animals

Main is far more frequently used. Unless students confuse these words, there is no need to introduce them.

The original meaning for **main** was "strong and powerful." A synonym is **chief**.

Mane comes from a root which means "neck."

Answers

1. *main*
2. *mane*
3. *mane*
4. *main*
5. *main*
6. *mane*
7. *main*
8. *main*
9. *main*
10. *main*
11. *mane*
12. *main*
13. *mane*
14. *main*
15. *main*
16. *mane*
17. *main*
18. *mane*
19. *mane*
20. *main*

meat – meet *p. 103*

Meet is on Spelling Plus list 15.
Recommended for grade 3.

meat *n.* the flesh of animals used as food
meet *v.* to encounter or come upon, to be introduced to
n. a gathering or meeting

Meet is much more frequently used than **meat**, generally as a verb.

Remember, "You can **eat meat**."

Answers

1. *meet*
2. *meat*
3. *meet*
4. *meet*
5. *meat*
6. *meat*
7. *meat*
8. *meet*
9. *meet*
10. *meat*
11. *meat*
12. *meet*
13. *meet*
14. *meat*
15. *meat*
16. *meet*
17. *meet*
18. *meat*
19. *meat*
20. *meat*

missed – mist *p. 104*

Miss is on Spelling Plus list 8.
Recommended for grade 4.

missed *v.* failed to hit, did miss
mist *n.* a thin fog just above the surface of the ground

Missed is more common than **mist**.

Missed is **miss** plus the inflectional ending **-ed**, making it a past tense form of the verb. Add the endings **-es** to form **misses** and **-ing** to form **missing**.

The original meaning of **mist** was "darkness."

Answers

1. *mist*
2. *missed*
3. *missed*
4. *mist*
5. *missed*
6. *missed*
7. *mist*
8. *missed*
9. *missed*
10. *missed*
11. *mist*
12. *mist*
13. *missed*
14. *mist*
15. *mist*
16. *missed*
17. *mist*
18. *missed*
19. *mist*
20. *mist*

new – knew *p. 105*

Spelling Plus list 33.
Recommended for grade 3.

new *adj.* not old
knew *v.* understood, was acquainted with, did know

Both of these words are *very* frequently used and confused.

Knew is from the Old English word **cnawan**. The **k** sound was pronounced, not silent as it is now. The word is related to **ken**, Scottish for "to know." Students may wish to pronounce the **k** in their minds as an aid to spelling.

Knew is the past tense of **know**. Other words which form the past tense in this way are:
blow – blew – blown
grow – grew – grown
throw – threw – thrown

Answers

1. *knew*
2. *new*
3. *new*
4. *new*
5. *knew*
6. *new*
7. *knew*
8. *knew*
9. *knew*
10. *new*
11. *new*
12. *knew*
13. *knew*
14. *new*
15. *knew*
16. *new*
17. *knew*
18. *new*
19. *knew*
20. *knew*

night – knight *p. 106*

Night is on Spelling Plus list 40.
Recommended for grade 4.

night *n.* opposite of *day*
knight *n.* a military man in the Middle Ages who wore armor

The word **night** is far more frequently used. **Knight** is used so infrequently that it isn't necessary to teach these homophones unless you are studying the Middle Ages.

The **gh** in both of these words was once a guttural sound similar to that in the Scottish word **loch**. This sound is no longer used in English.

The **k** in **knight** was once sounded. In Old English, it was spelled **cniht** and was pronounced rather like **kuh - nee - guh - tuh**. Students may use this old pronunciation while spelling.

Answers

1. *night*
2. *night*
3. *knight*
4. *night*
5. *knight*
6. *night*
7. *night*
8. *knight*
9. *night*
10. *night*
11. *night*
12. *knight*
13. *knight*
14. *night*
15. *night*
16. *knight*
17. *night*
18. *knight*
19. *knight*
20. *night*

no – know *p. 107*

***No** is on Spelling Plus list 10.*
***Know** is on Spelling Plus list 31.*
Recommended for grade 3.

no *adv. adj.* not any, opposite of *yes*
know *v.* to understand or be acquainted with

Both of these words are among the most common in English.

No is related to the word **none**.

Know is from the Old English word **cnawan**, which is related to the Scottish word **ken**, meaning "to know." The **k** sound was pronounced. Students may wish to say the **k** quietly as an aid to spelling, as long as they know the correct pronunciation of the word.

Remind students to capitalize words at the beginning of a sentence.

Answers

1. *know*
2. *no*
3. *No*
4. *know*
5. *No*
6. *know*
7. *no*
8. *know*
9. *no*
10. *know*
11. *no*
12. *know*
13. *no*
14. *know*
15. *know*
16. *no*
17. *know*
18. *no*
19. *know*
20. *no*

none – nun *p. 108*

Not on the Spelling Plus list.
Recommended for grade 4.

none *pron.* not any, not one
nun *n.* a woman vowed to the religious life

None is much more common than **nun**. There is no need to teach this set of homophones unless students demonstrate confusion in their writing.

None is from Old English **nan**, from **na** meaning "not" and **an** meaning "one." Link **none** with **one** as a mnemonic.

Answers

1. *nun*
2. *none*
3. *none*
4. *none*
5. *nun*
6. *none*
7. *nun*
8. *none*
9. *nun*
10. *none*
11. *none*
12. *nun*
13. *nun*
14. *none*
15. *none*
16. *none*
17. *nun*
18. *none*
19. *none*
20. *nun*

nose – knows *p. 109*

***Know** is on Spelling Plus list 31.*
Recommended for grade 3.

nose *n.* a part of the face, the organ of smell
knows *v.* understands, is acquainted with, does know

Knows is used much more common than **nose**. Teach this set only if there is evidence of confusion.

Nose is related to the word **nostril**.

Knows is **know** plus the ending **-s**. The ending **-ing** may be added to form **knowing**. **Know** comes from the Old English word **cnawan**, related to the Scottish word **ken** which means "to know." The **k** sound was pronounced. Students may pronounce it now as an aid to spelling, as long as they know the correct pronunciation of the word.

Answers

1. *knows*
2. *knows*
3. *nose*
4. *nose*
5. *knows*
6. *nose*
7. *nose*
8. *knows*
9. *knows*
10. *knows*
11. *nose*
12. *nose*
13. *knows*
14. *nose*
15. *knows*
16. *nose*
17. *knows*
18. *knows*
19. *nose*
20. *nose*

not – knot *p. 110*

***Not** is on Spelling Plus List 3.*
Recommended for grade 3.

not *adv.* in no way
knot *n.* a fastening made by tying

Not is used much more frequently than **knot**. Introduce these homophones when students begin using the word **knot** in writing.

Not is a shortened form of the old word **nought**. The spelling **not** was originally used only when the word was unstressed, but later came to be used for all forms of the word.

Knot is from Old English **cnotta** meaning "hard lump." The **k** sound was pronounced. Students who know the correct pronunciation may wish to sound the **k** as a help in spelling this word.

Answers

1. *not*
2. *knot*
3. *not*
4. *not*
5. *knot*
6. *not*
7. *knot*
8. *knot*
9. *not*
10. *knot*
11. *not*
12. *not*
13. *knot*
14. *not*
15. *knot*
16. *knot*
17. *knot*
18. *not*
19. *not*
20. *knot*

off – of *p. 111*

***Off** is on Spelling Plus list 8.*
***Of** is on Spelling Plus list 17.*
Recommended for grade 2.

off *adv. prep. adj.* opposite of *on*
of *prep.* from, with, containing

These words actually have quite different pronunciations, but they are frequently confused by students in writing. **Of** is the third most frequently used word in the English language. **Off** is also common.

Off was originally a variation of the word **of**. It was not differentiated until after 1600.

Clear pronunciation should help in avoiding confusion between these two words while writing.

Answers

1. *off*
2. *of*
3. *of*
4. *off*
5. *off*
6. *of*
7. *of*
8. *of*
9. *off*
10. *of*
11. *off*
12. *of*
13. *off*
14. *off*
15. *of*
16. *off*
17. *off*
18. *of*
19. *off*
20. *of*

oh – owe *p. 112*

***Oh** is on Spelling Plus list 17.*
Recommended for grade 3.

oh *interj.* an exclamation
owe *v.* to have a debt

Oh is used more frequently than **owe**.

Oh was once spelled **O** in English. It was spelled **oh** in Old French and Latin.

Owe is from Old English. Its original past tense was **ought**, and the meaning was "have to pay."

Since "Oh" is an interjection, it will generally be placed at the beginning of a sentence. Remind students to capitalize.

Answers

1. *owe*
2. *Oh*
3. *Oh*
4. *owe*
5. *owe*
6. *Oh*
7. *owe*
8. *Oh*
9. *Oh*
10. *Oh*
11. *Oh*
12. *owe*
13. *owe*
14. *owe*
15. *Oh*
16. *owe*
17. *Oh*
18. *owe*
19. *owe*
20. *Oh*

one – won *p. 113*

***One** is on Spelling Plus list 14.*
Recommended for grade 4.

one *n. adj.* the number 1
won *v.* was victorious, did win

One is used more frequently than **won**.

One was once pronounced with a long **o** as in the words **alone** and **only**. The pronunciation with a **w** is from a western English dialect in the 1500's. Other words beginning with **o**, such as **oak** and **oats**, were also pronounced with a **w**, but those pronunciations did not survive.

Won is the past tense of **win**. Link the two words.

One may also be used as a pronoun, as in, "One must work hard to succeed."

Answers

1. *won*
2. *won*
3. *one*
4. *one*
5. *one*
6. *won*
7. *won*
8. *one*
9. *won*
10. *one*
11. *one*
12. *one*
13. *won*
14. *one*
15. *won*
16. *one*
17. *one*
18. *won*
19. *won*
20. *won*

pail – pale *p. 114*

Not on the Spelling Plus list.
Recommended for grade 3.

pail *n.* a small bucket
pale *adj.* without much color

Pale is more common than **pail**, although neither word is very common.

The Latin form of **pale** is **pallid**.

Answers

1. *pail*
2. *pale*
3. *pail*
4. *pail*
5. *pale*
6. *pail*
7. *pale*
8. *pail*
9. *pale*
10. *pale*
11. *pale*
12. *pail*
13. *pale*
14. *pale*
15. *pail*
16. *pail*
17. *pail*
18. *pale*
19. *pail*
20. *pale*

pain – pane *p. 115*

Not on the Spelling Plus list.
Recommended for grade 3.

pain *n.* hurt
pane *n.* a piece or division, such as of a window

Pain is more common than **pane**.

Pain is from Old French and originally meant punishment. It is related to the word **penalty** as well as to the word **pine**, meaning "waste away through grief, pain or longing."

Pane originally meant a piece of cloth. It is closely related to the word **panel**, and can be linked to that word as an aid to meaning and spelling.

Answers

1. *pain*
2. *pain*
3. *pane*
4. *pain*
5. *pane*
6. *pain*
7. *pain*
8. *pane*
9. *pain*
10. *pane*
11. *pain*
12. *pain*
13. *pain*
14. *pane*
15. *pane*
16. *pain*
17. *pane*
18. *pain*
19. *pain*
20. *pain*

pair – pare – pear *p. 116*

Not on the Spelling Plus list.
Recommended for grade 3.

pair *n.* two
pare *v.* to cut or trim away, peel
pear *n.* a fruit

Pair is the most frequently used of these three words.

Pair comes from Latin through Old French. It is related to **par**, meaning "equal."

Pare is related to **prepare**, which means "to pare (peel) beforehand."

Answers

1. *pear*
2. *pair*
3. *pair*
4. *pare*
5. *pair*
6. *pear*
7. *pair*
8. *pair*
9. *pare*
10. *pear*
11. *pair*
12. *pair*
13. *pair*
14. *pear*
15. *pear*
16. *pair*
17. *pare*
18. *pear*
19. *pair*
20. *pear*

passed – past *p. 117*

***Passed** is on Spelling Plus list 57.*
Recommended for grade 5.

passed *v.* went by, through or beyond, did pass
past *n.* the time that has gone by
prep. by
adj. of a former time

Both of these words are frequently used and confused.

Passed is the verb **pass** plus the ending **-ed**, making it a past tense verb. In a sentence, if "did pass" has the same meaning, the correct homophone is **passed**. The endings **-es** and **-ing** may be added to **pass** to form **passes** and **passing**.

If "did pass" does *not* make sense, use **past**. Once, **past** had either spelling. Chaucer wrote, "The day is short and it is passed pryme."

Answers

1. *passed*
2. *past*
3. *past*
4. *past*
5. *passed*
6. *past*
7. *passed*
8. *passed*
9. *past*
10. *passed*
11. *past*
12. *passed*
13. *past*
14. *passed*
15. *past*
16. *past*
17. *passed*
18. *passed*
19. *passed*
20. *past*

patience – patients *p. 118*

***Patient** is on Spelling Plus list 61.*
Recommended for grade 6.

patience *n.* endurance with calmness, the ability to wait without complaining
patients *n.* people under a doctor's care

Both of these words come from Latin through Old French. The root of **patience** means "to suffer."

Patients is the plural form of the word **patient**. If the meaning of the word is "more than one patient" use **patients**.

Answers

1. *patients*
2. *patience*
3. *patients*
4. *patients*
5. *patience*
6. *patients*
7. *patience*
8. *patience*
9. *patients*
10. *patience*
11. *patients*
12. *patients*
13. *patience*
14. *patience*
15. *patients*
16. *patience*
17. *patients*
18. *patience*
19. *patients*
20. *patience*

pause – paws *p. 119*

Not on the Spelling Plus list.
Recommended for grade 4.

pause *n.* a temporary stop
v. to make a pause, stop temporarily
paws *n.* feet of four-footed animals with claws

Pause is used more frequently than **paws**.

Link **pause** to **cause** or **because**, as in, "What's the **cause** of this **pause**?"

Paws means more than one **paw** and is formed by adding **-s** to the word **paw**. Link **paws** to **claws** as a reminder of meaning as well as of spelling.

Answers

1. *pause*
2. *pause*
3. *paws*
4. *paws*
5. *pause*
6. *paws*
7. *pause*
8. *pause*
9. *paws*
10. *paws*
11. *pause*
12. *pause*
13. *pause*
14. *paws*
15. *pause*
16. *paws*
17. *paws*
18. *pause*
19. *paws*
20. *paws*

peace – piece *p. 120*

***Piece** is on Spelling Plus list 33.*
Recommended for grade 3.

peace *n.* freedom from war or conflict; calmness
piece *n.* a separate or detached portion, a part

These words are used with about the same frequency in English.

Peace is from the Latin **pax**.

Piece was spelled **pece** in Middle English. A mnemonic which helps with both meaning and spelling is, "A **piece** of **pie**."

Answers

1. *piece*
2. *piece*
3. *piece*
4. *peace*
5. *peace*
6. *peace*
7. *piece*
8. *piece*
9. *peace*
10. *piece*
11. *peace*
12. *peace*
13. *piece*
14. *peace*
15. *peace*
16. *piece*
17. *peace*
18. *piece*
19. *piece*
20. *peace*

peak – peek *p. 121*

Not on the Spelling Plus list.
Recommended for grade 3.

peak *n.* pointed extremity, highest place
peek *v.* to glance at something quickly, especially through an opening or from behind something

Peak is more common than **peek**.

The word **peak** comes from a word meaning "pointed." It is related to **pike**, which was a weapon with a long wooden shaft and a pointed head.

Note that **peek** has two **e**'s just as **look** has two **o**'s.

Answers

1. *peek*
2. *peak*
3. *peek*
4. *peak*
5. *peek*
6. *peak*
7. *peak*
8. *peek*
9. *peek*
10. *peak*
11. *peak*
12. *peak*
13. *peek*
14. *peek*
15. *peak*
16. *peak*
17. *peek*
18. *peak*
19. *peek*
20. *peak*

peal – peel *p. 122*

Not on the Spelling Plus list.
Recommended for grade 3.

peal *n.* a loud ringing, as of bells
v. to ring
peel *v.* to cut away the skin or covering of something
n. the rind or covering of a fruit or vegetable

Peel is more common than **peal**.

Peal is related to **appeal** and originally meant the ringing of a bell or bells as a summons to come.

Peel originally meant to strip or make bald. It was first a verb, and later became a noun.

Answers

1. *peal*
2. *peel*
3. *peel*
4. *peal*
5. *peel*
6. *peel*
7. *peel*
8. *peal*
9. *peel*
10. *peel*
11. *peel*
12. *peal*
13. *peel*
14. *peal*
15. *peel*
16. *peel*
17. *peel*
18. *peal*
19. *peel*
20. *peel*

plain – plane *p. 123*

Plain *is on Spelling Plus list 32.*
Recommended for grade 3.

plain *adj.* simple, ordinary, clear
n. an area of level country
plane *n.* short for *airplane*

Both of these words are fairly common.

Both of these words are ultimately from the Latin word **planus** meaning "flat."

Although **plane** has meanings other than "airplane," that is how it is most often used by students.

Answers

1. *plain*
2. *plane*
3. *plane*
4. *plain*
5. *plain*
6. *plain*
7. *plane*
8. *plain*
9. *plane*
10. *plain*
11. *plane*
12. *plane*
13. *plain*
14. *plane*
15. *plain*
16. *plane*
17. *plane*
18. *plain*
19. *plain*
20. *plain*

principal – principle *p. 124*

Spelling Plus list 68.
Recommended for grade 6.

principal *adj.* most important, main
n. main, first in rank, the amount of a debt not including interest
principle *n.* a rule or basic truth

Principal is more frequently used than **principle**.

Principle ends with **le**, as does **rule**. Any rule, truth, or pattern of conduct is a **principle**. For all other meanings, use the spelling **principal**.

Principal is from **prince** plus the suffix **-al** meaning "pertaining to." The word **main** has an **a** as does **principal**. The **principal** of a loan is the m**a**in part, the school **principal** is the m**a**in leader.

Answers

1. *principal*
2. *principal*
3. *principal*
4. *principal*
5. *principle*
6. *principle*
7. *principle*
8. *principal*
9. *principle*
10. *principal*
11. *principle*
12. *principle*
13. *principal*
14. *principal*
15. *principal*
16. *principal*
17. *principle*
18. *principle*
19. *principal*
20. *principal*

profit – prophet *p. 125*

Not on the Spelling Plus list.
Recommended for grade 5.

profit *n.* advantage, benefit, money left after expenses
v. to gain a benefit, make a profit
prophet *n.* a person who tells the future, often as revealed by God

Profit is used more frequently than **prophet**.

Profit comes from Latin through Old French. It is related to the word **proficient**.

Prophet comes from Greek through Latin and comes from word parts meaning "to speak before."

Answers

1. *profit*
2. *prophet*
3. *profit*
4. *prophet*
5. *profit*
6. *profit*
7. *prophet*
8. *prophet*
9. *profit*
10. *prophet*
11. *profit*
12. *profit*
13. *prophet*
14. *prophet*
15. *prophet*
16. *prophet*
17. *profit*
18. *profit*
19. *prophet*
20. *profit*

quite – quiet *p. 126*

Quite *is on Spelling Plus list 12.*
Quiet *is on Spelling Plus list 34.*
Recommended for grade 3.

quite *adv.* really
quiet *adj.* calm, not noisy

These words have different pronunciations, but are frequently confused by students because of the similarity in spelling. Both have the same Latin root, **quietus**. **Quite** is more frequently used than **quiet**.

Quite is a one-syllable word which was once a form of **quit**, meaning "free and clear." Imagine something which is "qu**ite** wh**ite**."

Quiet is a two-syllable word.

Clear pronunciation of these words will help with spelling.

Answers

1. *quiet*
2. *quite*
3. *quite*
4. *quiet*
5. *quite*
6. *quiet*
7. *quite*
8. *quiet*
9. *quiet*
10. *quite*
11. *quiet*
12. *quite*
13. *quite*
14. *quiet*
15. *quiet*
16. *quite*
17. *quiet*
18. *quite*
19. *quite*
20. *quiet*

rain – rein – reign *p. 127*

***Rain** is on Spelling Plus list 32.*
Recommended for grade 3.

rain *n.* water falling from the sky
v. to fall like rain
rein *n.* part of a horse's bridle
reign *v.* to rule with royal power

Rain is the most frequently used of these words. **Reign** is least used.

Rein is related to the word **retain**. Remember to use **re** for the kind of **re**in that **re**tains a horse.

Reign is related to the word **regal**, which means **royal**. **Regal** has a **g** as does **reign**.

Both **rein** and **reign** follow the rule: ***i** before **e** except after **c** or when sounded like **a** as in neighbor and weigh.* Can students say why?

Answers

1. *rein*
2. *reign*
3. *rein*
4. *rain*
5. *rain*
6. *reign*
7. *rain*
8. *rein*
9. *rain*
10. *reign*
11. *rain*
12. *reign*
13. *rain*
14. *rein*
15. *rein*
16. *rain*
17. *reign*
18. *rain*
19. *rein*
20. *reign*

raise – rays *p. 128*

***Raise** is on Spelling Plus list 32.*
Recommended for grade 3.

raise *v.* to lift, gather, or cause to rise, grow or bring up
rays *n.* thin beams of light

Raise is used much more frequently than **rays**.

Raise comes from Old Norse. The Old English equivalent was **rear**, which is still the preferred word when referring to **rearing** children. Link **raise** with **rise**. Just add an **a** after the **r** and before the **i**.

Ray is the base word **ray** plus the ending **-s** which makes it a plural noun. If "more than one ray" is the meaning in the sentence, use **rays**.

Answers

1. *rays*
2. *raise*
3. *rays*
4. *rays*
5. *raise*
6. *rays*
7. *rays*
8. *raise*
9. *raise*
10. *raise*
11. *rays*
12. *raise*
13. *rays*
14. *raise*
15. *raise*
16. *rays*
17. *rays*
18. *raise*
19. *rays*
20. *raise*

rap – wrap *p. 129*

Not on the Spelling Plus list.
Recommended for grade 4.

rap *v.* to strike or knock swiftly
n. a quick, sharp knock or tap
wrap *v.* to wind or fold a covering around something

Neither of these words is frequently used. **Wrap** is more common than **rap**.

Link **rap** to other words for sounds such as **tap**, **slap**, **clap**, and **flap**.

Answers

1. *rap*
2. *wrap*
3. *rap*
4. *wrap*
5. *wrap*
6. *wrap*
7. *rap*
8. *rap*
9. *wrap*
10. *rap*
11. *rap*
12. *wrap*
13. *rap*
14. *rap*
15. *wrap*
16. *wrap*
17. *wrap*
18. *rap*
19. *wrap*
20. *wrap*

read – red *p. 130*

***Read** is on Spelling Plus list 28.*
***Red** is on Spelling Plus list 5.*
Recommended for grade 3.

read *v.* got meaning from print using the eyes, did read
red *adj. n.* a color

Read is the more common of these two words.

Read is the past tense form of **to read**. Since the 1700's, the spelling for both past and present forms has been identical. The pronunciation, **read** – **read**, is the same as the pronunciation of **lead** – **led**.

Red was once pronounced with a long **e** and spelled **read**. The vowel was shortened as it was in **bread** and **dead**. The long **e** sound is preserved in surnames meaning **red**, such as **Reid** and **Read**.

Answers

1. *read*
2. *read*
3. *red*
4. *read*
5. *red*
6. *read*
7. *red*
8. *red*
9. *red*
10. *red*
11. *read*
12. *red*
13. *red*
14. *read*
15. *read*
16. *red*
17. *read*
18. *read*
19. *read*
20. *red*

reads – reeds *p. 131*

***Read** is on Spelling Plus list 28.*
Recommended for grade 3.

reads *v.* gets meaning from print using the eyes, does read
reeds *n.* tall slender grasses which grow on marshy lands

Reads is so much more common than **reeds** that there is little need to introduce this pair of homophones unless students demonstrate confusion in their writing.

Reads is **read** plus the ending **-s**. Other endings can be added to the base word to form **reading** and **reader**.

Reeds is **reed** plus the ending **-s**, making the word plural. If "more than one reed" is the meaning in the sentence, use **reeds**.

Answers

1. *reads*
2. *reeds*
3. *reads*
4. *reeds*
5. *reads*
6. *reeds*
7. *reads*
8. *reads*
9. *reeds*
10. *reeds*
11. *reads*
12. *reeds*
13. *reads*
14. *reads*
15. *reads*
16. *reeds*
17. *reeds*
18. *reads*
19. *reeds*
20. *reeds*

real – reel *p. 132*

***Real** is on Spelling Plus list 27.*
Recommended for grade 3.

real *adj.* genuine, true
reel *n.* a spool on which thread or line is wound
v. to wind on a reel

Real is far more common than **reel**, and may not need to be specifically introduced unless students demonstrate confusion in their writing.

Real came into English from Latin through Old French. The Latin word meant "pertaining to things." Overpronouncing this word with two syllables **re – al** can help with spelling.

Reel was originally a Scottish word for a winding instrument for thread or silk.

Answers

1. *real*
2. *reel*
3. *reel*
4. *real*
5. *real*
6. *reel*
7. *real*
8. *reel*
9. *real*
10. *real*
11. *reel*
12. *reel*
13. *real*
14. *reel*
15. *real*
16. *reel*
17. *real*
18. *reel*
19. *reel*
20. *real*

right – write *p. 133*

***Right** is on Spelling Plus list 40.*
***Write** is on Spelling Plus list 42.*
Recommended for grade 4.

right *adj.* just and correct, opposite of *left* when speaking of sides
n. that which a person has a just claim to
adv. straight, direct
write *v.* to form letters and words on paper

Both of these words are quite common in English. The word **write** has one specific meaning, while **right** may be used in a variety of ways. Use **right** for most meanings.

The first meaning of **write** was "engrave" because the first writing was done by scratching or engraving symbols on stone or wood with sharp tools.

Answers

1. *right*
2. *write*
3. *right*
4. *right*
5. *write*
6. *right*
7. *write*
8. *write*
9. *right*
10. *write*
11. *right*
12. *right*
13. *write*
14. *right*
15. *right*
16. *write*
17. *right*
18. *write*
19. *write*
20. *write*

ring – wring *p. 134*

Not on the Spelling Plus list.
Recommended for grade 4.

ring *n.* a circular object or line
v. to give forth a sound or cause something such as a bell to give forth a sound
wring *v.* squeeze, twist, wrench, wrest

Ring is used more frequently than **wring** in English. The noun **ring** and the verb **ring** are homonyms. They come from different roots.

The word **wring** comes from the same root as **wrong**. **Wring** was once used to describe a type of violent attack on a person. It now generally means to squeeze and twist something in order to force out water or any liquid.

Answers

1. *ring*
2. *ring*
3. *wring*
4. *ring*
5. *wring*
6. *wring*
7. *ring*
8. *wring*
9. *ring*
10. *ring*
11. *ring*
12. *wring*
13. *ring*
14. *wring*
15. *ring*
16. *ring*
17. *ring*
18. *wring*
19. *wring*
20. *ring*

road – rode *p. 135*

***Road** is on Spelling Plus list 38.*
Recommended for grade 4.

road *n.* a street or highway
rode *v.* was carried along in, did ride

Road is used more frequently than **rode**.

The word **road** is related to the word **ride**. A road was a way or path made for riding.

Rode is the irregular past tense form of **to ride**. It differs from **ride** by only one letter.

Answers

1. *rode*
2. *road*
3. *rode*
4. *road*
5. *road*
6. *rode*
7. *road*
8. *road*
9. *road*
10. *rode*
11. *rode*
12. *road*
13. *rode*
14. *road*
15. *road*
16. *rode*
17. *road*
18. *rode*
19. *rode*
20. *rode*

sail – sale *p. 136*

***Sale** is on Spelling Plus list 11.*
Recommended for grade 3.

sail *v.* to travel by sailboat
n. canvas sheet of a sailboat
sale *n.* having to do with selling

Sale is used more frequently than **sail**.

The word **sail** was originally a noun only. Later it became a verb, **to sail**.

Sale is closely related to the word **sell**. Both have to do with offering or exchanging something for money.

Answers

1. *sail*
2. *sail*
3. *sale*
4. *sail*
5. *sale*
6. *sale*
7. *sail*
8. *sale*
9. *sale*
10. *sail*
11. *sail*
12. *sale*
13. *sale*
14. *sail*
15. *sale*
16. *sail*
17. *sail*
18. *sale*
19. *sale*
20. *sail*

scene – seen *p. 137*

***Scene** is on Spelling Plus list 69.*
***Seen** is on Spelling Plus list 15.*
Recommended for grade 6.

scene *n.* a setting or place
seen *v.* perceived with the eyes

Seen is used much more frequently than **scene**.

Seen is from the word **see**. The two words should be linked as an aid to meaning as well as spelling.

Scene is from the Greek word **skene** through Latin **scena** and has to do with scenery and the stage.

Answers

1. *scene*
2. *seen*
3. *seen*
4. *scene*
5. *seen*
6. *scene*
7. *scene*
8. *seen*
9. *seen*
10. *seen*
11. *scene*
12. *seen*
13. *scene*
14. *seen*
15. *seen*
16. *scene*
17. *scene*
18. *scene*
19. *seen*
20. *scene*

sea – see *p. 138*

***Sea** is on Spelling Plus list 28.*
***See** is on Spelling Plus list 15.*
Recommended for grade 3.

sea *n.* a body of salt water smaller than an ocean
see *v.* to look at and perceive with the eyes

These two words were once pronounced differently. **See** is used more frequently than **sea**.

As a mnemonic, picture little eyes and eyelashes on the two **e**'s in **see**.

Answers

1. *see*
2. *see*
3. *sea*
4. *see*
5. *see*
6. *sea*
7. *sea*
8. *sea*
9. *sea*
10. *see*
11. *see*
12. *sea*
13. *see*
14. *see*
15. *see*
16. *sea*
17. *see*
18. *sea*
19. *sea*
20. *sea*

seam – seem *p. 139*

Seem is on Spelling Plus list 15.
Recommended for grade 3.

seam *n.* the line made by sewing two things together
seem *v.* to appear to be

Seem is used much more frequently than **seam**.

Seem can be linked to **see**, although the words are not related. Things you **see seem**, or appear, to be true.

Answers

1. *seem*
2. *seem*
3. *seam*
4. *seem*
5. *seam*
6. *seem*
7. *seam*
8. *seem*
9. *seem*
10. *seam*
11. *seem*
12. *seem*
13. *seem*
14. *seem*
15. *seam*
16. *seam*
17. *seem*
18. *seam*
19. *seem*
20. *seam*

sense – since *p. 140*

***Sense** is on Spelling Plus list 58.*
***Since** is on Spelling Plus list 55.*
Recommended for grade 5.

sense *n.* the ability to think or feel
v. to be or become aware of
since *conj. prep.* continuously from a certain time until now
adv. from then until now

These words are pronounced differently, one with a short **e** and one with a short **i**, but the difference is difficult to hear. **Since** is more often used, but both are common.

Sense is from the same Latin root as **sentence**. A **sentence** must make **sense**. Link these two words.

The spelling of **since** was changed in the 1500's to end with **-ce**. Possibly link it with **prince** in a mnemonic sentence.

Answers

1. *sense*
2. *since*
3. *sense*
4. *since*
5. *since*
6. *since*
7. *sense*
8. *since*
9. *sense*
10. *sense*
11. *since*
12. *sense*
13. *since*
14. *since*
15. *since*
16. *sense*
17. *sense*
18. *since*
19. *sense*
20. *sense*

sew – so – sow *p. 141*

***So** is on Spelling Plus list 10.*
Recommended for grade 4.

sew *v.* to join with a needle and thread
so *adv.* very
sow *v.* to plant

So is by far the most common of these three words. Teach this set of homophones when and if students demonstrate confusion in writing.

Sew rhymed with **new** and **sue** until the 1700's.

Sow comes from the same root as the word **seed**.

So can also be a conjunction, as in, "Please be quiet so I can sleep," or an interjection, "So!"

Answers

1. *so*
2. *sew*
3. *sow*
4. *so*
5. *so*
6. *sew*
7. *sow*
8. *sow*
9. *so*
10. *sew*
11. *sow*
12. *so*
13. *sew*
14. *sew*
15. *so*
16. *so*
17. *sow*
18. *sew*
19. *sew*
20. *sow*

soar – sore *p. 142*

Not on the Spelling Plus list.
Recommended for grade 3.

soar *v.* to rise or fly high into the air
sore *adj.* painful
n. a place where the skin is broken or inflamed

Students are more likely to use **sore** than **soar** in their writing.

Answers

1. *soar*
2. *sore*
3. *sore*
4. *soar*
5. *soar*
6. *sore*
7. *soar*
8. *soar*
9. *sore*
10. *sore*
11. *sore*
12. *soar*
13. *sore*
14. *soar*
15. *soar*
16. *soar*
17. *sore*
18. *soar*
19. *sore*
20. *sore*

some – sum *p. 143*

***Some** is on Spelling Plus list 14.*
Recommended for grade 2.

some *adj.* a certain number of
sum *n.* total amount, the result of addition
v. to summarize

Some is much more commonly used than **sum**.

In Old English, the word **some** was spelled **sum**. For legibility in handwritten manuscripts, Norman scribes changed **u** to **o** before and after **m**, **n**, **u**, **v** and **w**. This resulted in the modern spellings of such words as **some**, **come**, **love**, **done** and **from**.

Answers

1. *sum*
2. *some*
3. *some*
4. *sum*
5. *some*
6. *sum*
7. *some*
8. *some*
9. *sum*
10. *some*
11. *sum*
12. *some*
13. *some*
14. *sum*
15. *sum*
16. *some*
17. *some*
18. *some*
19. *sum*
20. *some*

son – sun *p. 144*

***Son** is on Spelling Plus list 50.*
Recommended for grade 5.

son *n.* a male child
sun *n.* the center of the solar system, from which comes heat and light

Son is used more frequently than **sun**, although both words are common.

Answers

1. *son*
2. *sun*
3. *sun*
4. *son*
5. *son*
6. *sun*
7. *son*
8. *sun*
9. *sun*
10. *sun*
11. *son*
12. *sun*
13. *son*
14. *sun*
15. *sun*
16. *son*
17. *son*
18. *son*
19. *son*
20. *sun*

stairs – stares *p. 145*

***Stairs** is on Spelling Plus list 51.*
Recommended for grade 5.

stairs *n.* steps in a staircase
stares *v.* looks fixedly at something, does stare

Stare is a more common word in English than **stair**.

Stairs is the plural form of the noun **stair**.

Stares is a form of the verb **stare**. The endings **-ed** and **-ing** can be added to **stare** after dropping the silent **e** to form **stared** and **staring**.

Answers

1. *stairs*
2. *stares*
3. *stairs*
4. *stairs*
5. *stares*
6. *stares*
7. *stairs*
8. *stares*
9. *stairs*
10. *stairs*
11. *stairs*
12. *stares*
13. *stairs*
14. *stares*
15. *stares*
16. *stares*
17. *stairs*
18. *stares*
19. *stairs*
20. *stares*

stationary – stationery *p. 146*

Not on the Spelling Plus list.
Recommended for grade 6.

stationary *adj.* having a fixed station, not moving
stationery *n.* writing paper

Neither of these words is especially frequent in English, but confusion between them is common. Both come from the root **station**.

Stationary is **station** plus the suffix **-ary**, meaning "pertaining to, connected with."

Stationery is one of two common English words ending with **-ery**. The other is **cemetery**. A **stationer** was at one time a bookseller, who sold writing materials as well as books. The letters **er** are in lett**er** as well as in station**ery**. You can write a lett**er** on station**ery**.

Answers

1. *stationery*
2. *stationary*
3. *stationery*
4. *stationery*
5. *stationary*
6. *stationary*
7. *stationary*
8. *stationery*
9. *stationery*
10. *stationery*
11. *stationary*
12. *stationary*
13. *stationery*
14. *stationary*
15. *stationery*
16. *stationary*
17. *stationary*
18. *stationery*
19. *stationary*
20. *stationery*

steak – stake *p. 147*

Not on the Spelling Plus list.
Recommended for grade 3.

steak *n.* a thick slice of meat
stake *n.* a pointed length of wood or metal
v. to mark a location with stakes

Neither of these words is especially common in English. Students would be more likely to use the word **steak** than **stake**.

Answers

1. *steak*
2. *steak*
3. *stake*
4. *steak*
5. *stake*
6. *stake*
7. *stake*
8. *steak*
9. *stake*
10. *steak*
11. *steak*
12. *steak*
13. *steak*
14. *stake*
15. *stake*
16. *stake*
17. *steak*
18. *steak*
19. *stake*
20. *stake*

steal – steel *p. 148*

Not on the Spelling Plus list.
Recommended for grade 3.

steal *v.* to rob
steel *n.* a kind of metal

Steel is used more frequently in English than **steal**, although children may write **steal** more often.

The endings -**s** and -**ing** can be added to the base word **steal** to form **steals** and **stealing**.

Answers

1. *steal*
2. *steal*
3. *steel*
4. *steel*
5. *steel*
6. *steal*
7. *steal*
8. *steel*
9. *steal*
10. *steal*
11. *steel*
12. *steal*
13. *steal*
14. *steal*
15. *steel*
16. *steel*
17. *steal*
18. *steal*
19. *steel*
20. *steel*

tacks – tax *p. 149*

Not on the Spelling Plus list.
Recommended for grade 4.

tacks *n.* small, short nails with broad heads
tax *n.* money paid to the government, a compulsory contribution
v. to assess a tax

Tax is the more commonly used of these two words.

Tacks is **tack** plus the ending -**s**. Other endings can be added to form **tacked** or **tacking**.

Answers

1. *tax*
2. *tacks*
3. *tax*
4. *tax*
5. *tacks*
6. *tacks*
7. *tax*
8. *tax*
9. *tax*
10. *tacks*
11. *tacks*
12. *tacks*
13. *tax*
14. *tacks*
15. *tax*
16. *tacks*
17. *tacks*
18. *tax*
19. *tax*
20. *tacks*

tail – tale *p. 150*

Not on the Spelling Plus list.
Recommended for grade 3.

tail *n.* an animal's tail or something which resembles it
tale *n.* a story

These words are used with approximately the same frequency in English.

Answers

1. *tale*
2. *tail*
3. *tale*
4. *tail*
5. *tail*
6. *tail*
7. *tale*
8. *tail*
9. *tale*
10. *tale*
11. *tale*
12. *tail*
13. *tail*
14. *tale*
15. *tail*
16. *tale*
17. *tail*
18. *tale*
19. *tale*
20. *tail*

then – than *p. 151*

Then *is on Spelling Plus list 5.*
Than *is on Spelling Plus list 4.*
Recommended for grade 1.

then *adv. n.* at that time, next in time
than *conj. prep.* a word used to show comparison

Although these words are pronounced differently, children often do not hear the difference. Both words are used frequently in English.

These two words were once identical, and were not differentiated until around 1700. The Dutch word **dan**, from the same source, still has both meanings.

Careful pronunciation may be an aid to spelling.

Answers

1. *than*
2. *then*
3. *then*
4. *than*
5. *than*
6. *than*
7. *then*
8. *than*
9. *then*
10. *then*
11. *than*
12. *then*
13. *than*
14. *then*
15. *than*
16. *then*
17. *than*
18. *than*
19. *than*
20. *then*

there – their *p. 152*

There *is on Spelling Plus list 13.*
Their *is on Spelling Plus list 18.*
Recommended for grade 2.

there *adv.* in that place, opposite of *here*
their *adj.* belonging to them

These are among the most confused words in English. Both begin with the letters **the**.

Link **there** with **here** and **where**. All of these words refer to a place.

Their has to do with belonging, or possession. It is one of the most often misspelled words by high school students, and should be reviewed continuously throughout the elementary grades.

Answers

1. *their*
2. *there*
3. *their*
4. *there*
5. *there*
6. *their*
7. *there*
8. *their*
9. *there*
10. *their*
11. *there*
12. *there*
13. *their*
14. *there*
15. *their*
16. *their*
17. *there*
18. *their*
19. *there*
20. *their*

there – they're – their *p. 153*

There *is on Spelling Plus list 13.*
They're *is on Spelling Plus list 22.*
Their *is on Spelling Plus list 18.*
Recommended for grade 2.

there *adv.* in that place, opposite of *here*
they're contraction of *they are*
their *adj.* belonging to them

These are among the most used and confused words in English. All begin with the letters **the**.

There refers to place. **Their** has to do with possession, or belonging.

To form a contraction from **they are**, replace the **a** in **are** with an apostrophe and move the two words together.

Remind students to capitalize any word at the beginning of a sentence.

Answers

1. *There*
2. *Their*
3. *they're*
4. *their*
5. *there*
6. *They're*
7. *There*
8. *They're*
9. *their*
10. *They're*
11. *there*
12. *their*
13. *They're*
14. *there*
15. *their*
16. *they're*
17. *they're*
18. *their*
19. *there*
20. *there*

threw – through *p. 154*

Threw *is on Spelling Plus list 33.*
Through *is on Spelling Plus list 41.*
Recommended for grade 4.

threw *v.* caused to fly through the air, did throw
through *prep. adv.* from end to end or side to side

Through is used more frequently than **threw**.

Threw is the irregular past tense form of **throw**. The words differ by just one letter and they should be linked. Other words which form the past in this way include:
blow – blew – blown
grow – grew – grown
know – knew – known

Through can possibly be linked with **rough**.

Answers

1. *threw*
2. *through*
3. *threw*
4. *through*
5. *through*
6. *threw*
7. *through*
8. *through*
9. *through*
10. *threw*
11. *through*
12. *through*
13. *threw*
14. *through*
15. *threw*
16. *through*
17. *threw*
18. *through*
19. *threw*
20. *through*

to – two *p. 155*

***To** is on Spelling Plus list 10.*
***Two** is on Spelling Plus list 21.*
Recommended for grade 2.

to *prep.* toward, for, as far as
two *adj.* the number 2

To is one of the most frequently used words in the English language. **Two** is also a very common word.

To can be a preposition or an "infinitive marker" coming before the infinitive form of a verb, as in **to know**, **to think**.

The **w** in **two** was once pronounced, as it is in **twin** and **twice**. Link **two** with **twin** as an aid in remembering this spelling and meaning.

Answers

1. *to*
2. *two*
3. *to*
4. *two*
5. *two*
6. *to*
7. *to*
8. *to*
9. *two*
10. *to*
11. *to*
12. *two*
13. *to*
14. *to*
15. *to*
16. *two*
17. *two*
18. *to*
19. *to*
20. *to*

to – too – two *p. 156*

***To** is on Spelling Plus list 10.*
***Too** is on Spelling Plus list 30.*
***Two** is on Spelling Plus list 21.*
Recommended for grade 3.

to *prep.* toward, for, as far as
too *adv.* more than enough, also
two *adj.* the number 2

To is one of the most frequently used words in the English language. **Too** is the least common of these three words.

See the previous lesson for information on **to** and **two**.

Too is a stressed form of the word **to** with a different spelling. A mnemonic is, "**Too** has **too** many **o**'s."

Answers

1. *too*
2. *two*
3. *to*
4. *to*
5. *too*
6. *to*
7. *two*
8. *to*
9. *too*
10. *too*
11. *to*
12. *too*
13. *too*
14. *two*
15. *too*
16. *to*
17. *too*
18. *too*
19. *two*
20. *to*

toad – towed *p. 157*

Not on the Spelling Plus list.
Recommended for grade 3.

toad *n.* a frog-like animal
towed *v.* pulled with a rope or chain, did tow

Neither of these words is especially common in English.

Toad is from the Old English word **tade**, also the source of **tadpole**.

Towed is the past tense form of **tow**, formed by adding -**ed** to **tow**. The endings -**s** and -**ing** can be added to **tow** to form **tows** and **towing**. If the word **pulled** can be substituted in a sentence, use **towed**.

Answers

1. *toad*
2. *towed*
3. *toad*
4. *toad*
5. *towed*
6. *toad*
7. *towed*
8. *towed*
9. *towed*
10. *toad*
11. *towed*
12. *towed*
13. *toad*
14. *toad*
15. *towed*
16. *toad*
17. *toad*
18. *toad*
19. *towed*
20. *towed*

toes – tows *p. 158*

Not on the Spelling Plus list.
Recommended for grade 3.

toes *n.* the digits at the end of the foot
tows *v.* pulls with a rope or chain, does tow

Neither of these words is especially common in English. **Toes** is somewhat more common than **tows**.

Toes is the plural form of the noun **toe** and means "more than one toe."

Tows is an inflected form of the verb **tow** and means "does tow." The endings -**ed** and -**ing** can be added to **tow** to form **towed** and **towing**. If the word **pulls** can be substituted in a sentence, use **tows**.

Answers

1. *tows*
2. *tows*
3. *toes*
4. *toes*
5. *tows*
6. *toes*
7. *toes*
8. *toes*
9. *toes*
10. *tows*
11. *tows*
12. *toes*
13. *tows*
14. *tows*
15. *toes*
16. *tows*
17. *toes*
18. *tows*
19. *tows*
20. *toes*

wade – weighed — *p. 159*

Not on the Spelling Plus list.
Recommended for grade 6.

wade *v.* to walk through water or any resistant substance
weighed *v.* found the weight of, did weigh

Weighed is more common than **wade**.

Wade is a base word to which inflectional endings can be added to form **wades**, **waded**, and **wading**.

Weighed is the past tense form of the base word **weigh**. Other inflectional endings can be added to **weigh** to make **weighs** and **weighing**.

The **gh** in **weighed** once had a guttural sound, the stopped **g**. This sound no longer exists in English.

Answers

1. *weighed*
2. *wade*
3. *weighed*
4. *weighed*
5. *wade*
6. *weighed*
7. *wade*
8. *wade*
9. *weighed*
10. *wade*
11. *wade*
12. *wade*
13. *weighed*
14. *wade*
15. *wade*
16. *weighed*
17. *wade*
18. *weighed*
19. *weighed*
20. *weighed*

waist – waste — *p. 160*

Not on the Spelling Plus list.
Recommended for grade 3.

waist *n.* middle part of the body
waste *n.* useless or discarded material, a wasting or being wasted
v. to destroy or use up needlessly

Waste is used more frequently than **waist**.

Waist was spelled a variety of ways in Middle England, including **wast**, **waast**, and **waste**. The spelling **waist** was rare before Samuel Johnson's first English dictionary.

The word **waste** originally meant uncultivated desert land.

Remind students that a word should be capitalized at the beginning of a quoted sentence.

Answers

1. *waist*
2. *waste*
3. *waist*
4. *waist*
5. *waste*
6. *waist*
7. *waste*
8. *Waste*
9. *waste*
10. *waist*
11. *waste*
12. *waste*
13. *waist*
14. *waste*
15. *waist*
16. *waist*
17. *waste*
18. *waist*
19. *waste*
20. *waist*

wait – weight — *p. 161*

***Wait** is on Spelling Plus list 32.*
***Weight** is on Spelling Plus list 62.*
Recommended for grade 6.

wait *v.* to stay in a place ready for something to happen
weight *n.* the heaviness of something

Wait is used more frequently than **weight**.

Link **weight** with **eight**. A mnemonic sentence, "His **weight** was **eight** hundred pounds."

Answers

1. *weight*
2. *wait*
3. *wait*
4. *weight*
5. *weight*
6. *weight*
7. *wait*
8. *weight*
9. *wait*
10. *wait*
11. *wait*
12. *wait*
13. *weight*
14. *weight*
15. *wait*
16. *weight*
17. *wait*
18. *weight*
19. *weight*
20. *wait*

way – weigh — *p. 162*

***Way** is on Spelling Plus list 13.*
Recommended for grade 6.

way *n.* a means of passing from place to place or a manner of doing something
weigh *v.* to find the heaviness of something with a scale

Way is used more frequently than **weigh**.

Link **weigh** with **weight** which should be linked with **eight**.

Answers

1. *weigh*
2. *way*
3. *way*
4. *weigh*
5. *way*
6. *weigh*
7. *weigh*
8. *way*
9. *weigh*
10. *way*
11. *weigh*
12. *way*
13. *way*
14. *way*
15. *weigh*
16. *weigh*
17. *way*
18. *weigh*
19. *way*
20. *weigh*

weak – week *p. 163*

***Weak** is on Spelling Plus list 27.*
***Week** is on Spelling Plus list 15.*
Recommended for grade 3.

weak *adj.* not strong
week *n.* seven days

Week is used more frequently than **weak**.

Answers

1. *week*
2. *weak*
3. *week*
4. *week*
5. *weak*
6. *week*
7. *week*
8. *weak*
9. *weak*
10. *week*
11. *week*
12. *weak*
13. *week*
14. *week*
15. *weak*
16. *week*
17. *week*
18. *weak*
19. *week*
20. *weak*

weather – whether *p. 164*

***Weather** is on Spelling Plus list 39.*
***Whether** is on Spelling Plus list 23.*
Recommended for grade 4.

weather *n.* climate, rain, storms, etc.
whether *conj.* used to introduce alternatives, as in *whether or not*

These words have such similar pronunciations that students often confuse them. Also, children tend to mix the spellings, writing **wheather** or **wether**.

A mnemonic for **weather** is, "We **eat** in all kinds of w**eat**her."

The **wh** in **whether** was once spelled as **hw**, which better reflects the pronunciation. Have students aspirate the **wh** as an aid to spelling. A mnemonic is, "I wonder wh**ether** they're tog**ether**."

Answers

1. *whether*
2. *weather*
3. *weather*
4. *whether*
5. *whether*
6. *weather*
7. *weather*
8. *whether*
9. *whether*
10. *weather*
11. *whether*
12. *whether*
13. *weather*
14. *whether*
15. *weather*
16. *whether*
17. *weather*
18. *whether*
19. *weather*
20. *whether*

were – we're *p. 165*

***Were** is on Spelling Plus list 13.*
Recommended for grade 2.

were *v.* a form of *to be,* the past of *are,* as in "They were gone."
we're contraction for *we are*

Both of these words are very frequently used. They may or may not be pronounced identically.

Whenever **we are** can be substituted in a sentence, use **we're**.

Answers

1. *were*
2. *we're*
3. *were*
4. *we're*
5. *we're*
6. *were*
7. *we're*
8. *were*
9. *were*
10. *we're*
11. *were*
12. *we're*
13. *we're*
14. *were*
15. *were*
16. *were*
17. *we're*
18. *were*
19. *we're*
20. *we're*

where – were *p. 166*

***Where** is on Spelling Plus list 23.*
***Were** is on Spelling Plus list 13.*
Recommended for grade 2.

where *adv.* in or at what place
were *v.* a form of *to be,* the past of *are,* as in "They were gone."

These words are not pronounced the same, but are frequently confused in writing nevertheless. **Were** is used more frequently than **where**, but both words are quite common.

Link **where** with **here** and **there**. All have the letters **here** and all refer to place.

Remind students to capitalize the first word in a sentence.

Answers

1. *Where*
2. *were*
3. *were*
4. *Where*
5. *were*
6. *Were*
7. *Where*
8. *were*
9. *were*
10. *Where*
11. *were*
12. *where*
13. *were*
14. *where*
15. *Were*
16. *were*
17. *Where*
18. *were*
19. *where*
20. *where*

which – witch *p. 167*

***Which** is on Spelling Plus list 23.*
Recommended for grade 4.

which *pron. adj.* what one
witch *n.* a woman supposedly having supernatural power through the devil or evil spirits

Children may not pronounce these words clearly enough to hear the difference. Students may mix the spellings and write **whitch** or **wich**. **Which** is a *much* more common word than **witch**.

The **wh** in **which** was once spelled with an **hw**. Have students aspirate the **wh** to remember the spelling.

Witch is a variation of **wicce**.

Remind students to capitalize the first word in a sentence.

Answers

1. *which*
2. *witch*
3. *witch*
4. *Which*
5. *which*
6. *witch*
7. *Which*
8. *which*
9. *witch*
10. *Which*
11. *witch*
12. *Which*
13. *which*
14. *witch*
15. *Which*
16. *Which*
17. *witch*
18. *Which*
19. *which*
20. *witch*

whose – who's *p. 168*

Spelling Plus list 23.
Recommended for grade 2.

whose *pron.* belonging to whom
who's contraction of *who is* or *who has*

Both of these words are common in English. They are very frequently confused. An **'s** is added to a noun to form a possessive, but not to the word **who**. **Whose** is the possessive pronoun.

Whose can be linked to **hose** with the mnemonic sentence, "**Whose hose** are these?"

If **who is** or **who has** can be substituted in a sentence, use **who's**.

Remind students to capitalize the first word in a sentence.

Answers

1. *Who's*
2. *Whose*
3. *Whose*
4. *whose*
5. *who's*
6. *Who's*
7. *Whose*
8. *Who's*
9. *Whose*
10. *Whose*
11. *Who's*
12. *Who's*
13. *Whose*
14. *Who's*
15. *who's*
16. *whose*
17. *Whose*
18. *Whose*
19. *who's*
20. *whose*

wood – would *p. 169*

***Would** is on Spelling Plus list 21.*
Recommended for grade 2.

wood *n.* lumber or timber
would *v.* from the word *will,* as in "He would not say."

Would is so much more common than **wood** and has such a different meaning that students may not have trouble with these words. Teach this set only if students show confusion.

Would was spelled **wolde** in Old English. The **l** was pronounced. **Would** is related to **will**. Link it with **could** (related to **can**) and **should** (related to **shall**).

Answers

1. *wood*
2. *would*
3. *wood*
4. *wood*
5. *would*
6. *would*
7. *wood*
8. *would*
9. *would*
10. *wood*
11. *would*
12. *wood*
13. *wood*
14. *would*
15. *would*
16. *would*
17. *wood*
18. *would*
19. *wood*
20. *wood*

your – you're *p. 170*

***Your** is on Spelling Plus list 8.*
***You're** is on Spelling Plus list 22.*
Recommended for grade 2.

your *adj.* belonging to you
you're contraction for *you are*

Both of these words are frequently used and confused.

Link **your** with **our**. Both words have the letters **our**. Both show possession.

If **you are** can be substituted in the sentence, use **you're**.

Remind students to capitalize the first word in a sentence.

Answers

1. *Your*
2. *you're*
3. *You're*
4. *your*
5. *Your*
6. *your*
7. *You're*
8. *You're*
9. *Your*
10. *your*
11. *you're*
12. *You're*
13. *Your*
14. *your*
15. *You're*
16. *Your*
17. *your*
18. *You're*
19. *you're*
20. *You're*

Name____

Date____

Accept — Except

1. The club will ____________________ all donations.
2. Everyone was invited to the party ____________________ Pam.
3. I will ____________________ your offer.
4. All of the girls ____________________ Christina may line up now.
5. Will you ____________________ this gift from me?
6. All of the houses ____________________ ours have gardens.
7. Everyone ____________________ you has brown hair.
8. I will ____________________ the job offer.
9. Everyone can go ____________________ me. I have to work.
10. All of our guests ____________________ the little children are fishing.
11. He will surely ____________________ your invitation.
12. Sure, I'll ____________________ a ride to school with you.
13. No one is allowed to come ____________________ my sister.
14. I will ____________________ your apology.
15. I like it ____________________ for the color.
16. I have to work every day ____________________ Tuesday.
17. I am certainly not going to ____________________ your excuses.
18. He remembered everything ____________________ his tennis shoes.
19. The teacher won't ____________________ any late work.
20. I finished everything ____________________ my math.

Name____

Date____

Access — Excess

1. Do you have ____________________ to the conference room?
2. It is not good to eat or drink to ____________________.
3. The price is in ____________________ of a million dollars.
4. Wheelchair ____________________ is through the door to the left.
5. Snowfall in Valdez, Alaska may be in ____________________ of 45 feet!
6. Only close family members have ____________________ to the keys.
7. The spies worked hard to gain ____________________ to the files.
8. Many pro basketball players are in ____________________ of 6'6" tall.
9. They gave their ____________________ clothing to the Salvation Army.
10. We have ____________________ food. Would you like some?
11. Only students have ____________________ to the library.
12. I don't have ____________________ to that information.
13. The ____________________ heat is used to generate electricity.
14. The government often sells ____________________ food to other countries.
15. The only ____________________ to the attic is through the roof of the storage room.
16. Only members have ____________________ to the discount store.
17. The business did well because of its easy ____________________.
18. His medical problems were caused by ____________________ weight.
19. They had to leave their ____________________ baggage behind.
20. Public ____________________ to the river is guaranteed.

Name____

Date____

Ad — Add

1. In math, they're learning how to ____________________ fractions.
2. I'm confused. This doesn't ____________________ up!
3. We'll put an ____________________ in the lost and found about the cat.
4. We're planning to ____________________ on to the house.
5. The ____________________ says flowers will be half price on Friday.
6. Here's a want ____________________ for a nurse.
7. He doesn't ____________________ very well.
8. They placed an __________________ in the newspaper to sell the couch.
9. Please ____________________ this to my total.
10. Every tobacco ____________________ has a warning about the dangers.
11. Companies usually run the same TV ________________ again and again.
12. I'll ____________________ that to my list of things to do.
13. He has ten new baseball cards to ___________________ to his collection.
14. Jerry had several good ideas to ____________________.
15. Your ____________________ said the sale would end tomorrow!
16. That ____________________ won an award for being so funny.
17. A full-page ____________________ in a magazine can cost thousands of dollars.
18. The ____________________ will run for two weeks.
19. The waitress forgot to ____________________ the price of our drinks.
20. Children learn to ____________________ before they learn to multiply.

Name____

Date____

Addition — Edition

1. I think ____________________ is a lot easier than subtraction.
2. You can find the answer by using ____________________.
3. I like the morning ____________________ of the newspaper better.
4. The first ____________________ of this magazine came out last month.
5. We are practicing our ____________________ facts.
6. This is the latest ____________________ of the World Book Encyclopedia.
7. The author will autograph the first ____________________ of his book.
8. We are learning ____________________ of fractions.
9. Simple ____________________ proved the answer was correct.
10. The newest ____________________ of collector plates is now available.
11. I like to watch the late ____________________ of the news on TV.
12. The builders just began work on an ____________________ to our house.
13. The March ____________________ of Reader's Digest was wonderful!
14. You must know ____________________ in order to succeed in this job.
15. John is the latest ____________________ to our class.
16. The ____________________ of an extra wing made the school larger.
17. The second ____________________ of the book was printed in 2005.
18. Some magazines print a large-type ____________________ for people who have trouble seeing.
19. I bought the hardcover ____________________ of the book.
20. In ____________________, we've invited three musicians to the party.

Name____

Date____

Affect — Effect

1. Aspirin doesn't seem to ____________________ her too much.
2. This disease will ____________________ everyone who comes near you.
3. The drug had a bad ____________________ on the patient.
4. Tides are an ____________________ of the moon's gravitational pull on the earth.
5. The ____________________ of the fight was a bloody nose for John.
6. I hope this doesn't ____________________ your decision.
7. This rain could ____________________ our weekend plans.
8. The spanking didn't have much ____________________ on his behavior.
9. I hope this idea will ____________________ the outcome.
10. We were wondering how the news would ____________________ him.
11. The speaker's tears seemed to ____________________ the crowd.
12. The spicy food had a bad ____________________ on the little boy.
13. I really wanted to ____________________ your decision at the time.
14. The bomb had a terrible ____________________ on the city.
15. The ____________________ of this chemical is deadly.
16. It seemed impossible to ____________________ him.
17. The ball hit her hard, and the ____________________ was a broken arm.
18. Why does walking ____________________ your feet as it does?
19. I'm not sure what ____________________ this will have.
20. Nothing she did seemed to ____________________ the boss.

Name____

Date____

Allowed — Aloud

1. It's against the rules to talk ____________________ during class.
2. I'm sorry, but fishing isn't ____________________ in this stream.
3. No one is ____________________ to enter without a pass.
4. We are not ____________________ to run in the halls.
5. Would you please read ____________________ from page 25?
6. Rock-throwing is never ____________________ on school grounds.
7. He repeated the list ____________________ to himself.
8. Mary wrote the phone number, saying each numeral ________________.
9. Smoking is not ____________________ in public buildings.
10. It was difficult to say ____________________ what was in his mind.
11. Visitors are ____________________ to enter through a special door.
12. He was talking ____________________ to himself.
13. Please repeat that sentence ____________________ to the class.
14. No dogs are ____________________ inside.
15. My big brother is ____________________ to do many things I can't.
16. At first they whispered, then they began to talk ____________________.
17. Their mother ____________________ them to order anything they chose.
18. Be careful. We might be caught if we talk ____________________.
19. People can talk without speaking ____________________ if they know sign language.
20. I wasn't ____________________ to try out for the team.

Name____

Date____

Ant — Aunt

1. His ____________________ is a doctor.
2. An ____________________ had already discovered our picnic basket.
3. There is a kind of ____________________ in Africa that marches in long lines like an army.
4. Jane's ____________________ is visiting from Florida.
5. I accidentally stood on an ____________________ pile.
6. An ____________________ bit me!
7. Sally was only 15 when she became an ____________________.
8. I watched a red ____________________ attack a bug.
9. John's ____________________ works at the telephone company.
10. Our ____________________ lives in California.
11. My mom was not happy to see an ____________________ on the counter.
12. I'm going to stay on a farm with my ____________________ and uncle.
13. Is it more painful to be bitten by an ____________________ or a spider?
14. The ____________________ has very great strength for its size.
15. Only the queen ____________________ lays eggs.
16. Is that lady your ____________________?
17. My ____________________ always kisses me on the nose.
18. A carpenter ____________________ makes tunnels in wood.
19. I have two uncles, but just one ____________________.
20. Who is your favorite ____________________?

Name____

Date____

Are — Our

1. That is ____________________ new car.
2. We ____________________ going out to eat.
3. Mike likes ____________________ house a lot.
4. Please don't walk on ____________________ lawn.
5. The trees ____________________ covered with snow.
6. Who ____________________ they?
7. She will help us with ____________________ work.
8. You ____________________ my best friend.
9. Why ____________________ you so sad?
10. They ____________________ not here today.
11. Mrs. Johnson is ____________________ teacher.
12. Where is ____________________ pizza?
13. How ____________________ you?
14. Mother is washing ____________________ clothes.
15. Jack and Jim ____________________ brothers.
16. What ____________________ they doing?
17. I think ____________________ school is great!
18. We have to clean ____________________ rooms every week.
19. No one can beat ____________________ team!
20. You ____________________ not in trouble.

Name____

Date____

Ate — Eight

1. He ____________________ the salad but not the dessert.
2. My brother is ____________________ years old.
3. I think it was something I ____________________.
4. My friend ____________________ all of the candy.
5. There were ____________________ players on the team.
6. He works hard for ____________________ hours each day.
7. They ____________________ everything on the table.
8. She drew a monster with ____________________ eyes.
9. A spider has ____________________ legs.
10. She ____________________ too much popcorn.
11. It will cost almost ____________________ dollars.
12. We ____________________ dinner at 5:00.
13. The dog ____________________ all of the leftovers.
14. The spaceship will blast off in just ____________________ minutes.
15. The boys ____________________ too much.
16. I bought ____________________ new light bulbs.
17. Our friends ____________________ fish every day last year.
18. The doctor wants to know what you ____________________.
19. I wonder why they ____________________ so early.
20. I read ____________________ books during vacation.

Name____

Date____

Be — Bee

1. I see a ____________________.
2. Will you ____________________ there?
3. I want to ____________________ a football player.
4. That ____________________ stung my foot!
5. A ____________________ flew into the house.
6. It can't ____________________ true!
7. Who wants to ____________________ first?
8. We will have to ____________________ quiet.
9. I hear a ____________________ buzzing.
10. Please ____________________ good today.
11. Will you ____________________ my friend?
12. It will ____________________ a nice day.
13. A ____________________ is on the flower.
14. My mom is afraid when she sees a ____________________.
15. My dog can ____________________ a pest sometimes.
16. That will ____________________ fine.
17. A ____________________ came in the car window.
18. Don't ____________________ afraid.
19. There will ____________________ three cats at the house.
20. No one can ____________________ that strong!

Name____

Date____

Bear — Bare

1. Most of the Sahara Desert is ____________________ ground.
2. A huge ____________________ stood up in the bushes.
3. I can't ____________________ to see you look so sad.
4. His head was ____________________.
5. The old ____________________ and her cub were safely in their den.
6. It feels good to walk through soft grass with ____________________ feet.
7. The pain was almost too much to ____________________.
8. There were ____________________ tracks near the house that morning.
9. We're supposed to be careful not to disturb the ____________________.
10. It was late fall and the aspen trees were ____________________.
11. His ____________________ back was beginning to burn in the sun.
12. She won't go camping because she's afraid a ____________________ might attack.
13. The cupboards were ____________________.
14. The polar ____________________ is an excellent swimmer.
15. That horse can't ____________________ such a heavy load.
16. The top of the mountain was ____________________ of snow.
17. There was a dancing ____________________ in the circus.
18. The paint had peeled off, leaving ____________________ wood.
19. The black ____________________ is good at climbing trees.
20. The men were hunting for ____________________.

Name____

Date____

Beat — Beet

1. Listen to the ____________________ of the music.
2. I can ____________________ you anytime.
3. You must ____________________ the eggs before adding them to the mixture.
4. My mother cooked a ____________________ for dinner.
5. Our team ____________________ the champions.
6. The recipe called for one ____________________.
7. Plant your ____________________ seeds about one inch under the soil.
8. Nobody can ____________________ us!
9. Both the root and the greens of a ____________________ can be eaten.
10. The policemen ____________________ on the door.
11. The hail ____________________ down the flowers.
12. Some people like pickled ____________________ roots.
13. A sugar ____________________ is large and light tan.
14. He slowly ____________________ his fist on the table.
15. People once used ____________________ juice to make dye.
16. She was running to ____________________ her brothers to the mailbox.
17. Janie can ____________________ anyone at spelling.
18. The Denver Broncos just ____________________ the Dallas Cowboys!
19. More than half of our sugar comes from the sugar __________________.
20. Her family loves ____________________ soup.

Name____

Date____

Berry — Bury

1. The pirates planned to __________________ the treasure on an island.
2. The directions say to ____________________ the seeds a half inch deep.
3. We love to go ____________________ picking.
4. There is only one ____________________ on this whole bush.
5. In the wilderness, it is best to burn and ____________________ any garbage that cannot be carried out.
6. That red ____________________ is poisonous.
7. The dog took the bone to ____________________ it.
8. What kind of _________________ would you like to put on your cereal?
9. The ____________________ juice stained my teeth.
10. My mom makes wild ____________________ jam.
11. A cemetery is a place to ____________________ people.
12. After you clean the fish, please ____________________ the remains.
13. The electric company prefers to ____________________ power lines.
14. Are grapes a kind of ____________________?
15. The ____________________ grows after the flower drops off.
16. The criminal was trying to ____________________ the evidence.
17. What kind of ____________________ are we looking for?
18. I love ____________________ pie.
19. This ____________________ can be used to make syrup.
20. Be sure to ____________________ the ashes before leaving a campfire.

Name____

Date____

Blew — Blue

1. The sky was a deep ____________________.
2. The wind ____________________ down some trees in our yard.
3. I ____________________ up several balloons for the party.
4. Her favorite color is ____________________.
5. Glacier ice often looks ____________________.
6. Where's my ____________________ jacket?
7. He ____________________ out all of the candles on his birthday cake.
8. I live in the ____________________ house on the corner.
9. We ____________________ bubbles yesterday.
10. The old man ____________________ out the lantern and went to bed.
11. You mix ____________________ and yellow paint to get green.
12. The ____________________ towel belongs to Jim.
13. The old shed ____________________ down in the storm.
14. They finally ____________________ up that old building.
15. The campers ____________________ gently on the coals of the fire.
16. I love those delicate ____________________ flowers.
17. The wind ____________________ so hard that I could hardly walk.
18. He's still black and ____________________ from his skiing accident.
19. All of the papers ____________________ away.
20. The deep ____________________ sea can be dangerous at times.

Name____

Date____

Board — Bored

1. The children were ____________________ with television.
2. I was ____________________ yesterday.
3. Would you help me measure this ____________________?
4. Were you ____________________ by the speech?
5. I need to buy a long ____________________, please.
6. This ____________________ is just what I need.
7. We ran over a big ____________________.
8. Third graders would probably be ____________________ in a first grade class.
9. The carpenter needed one more ____________________ to finish the job.
10. They don't know what it's like to be __________________.
11. People often feel ____________________ when they don't understand.
12. He cut the ____________________ into eight small pieces.
13. People with imagination are almost never ____________________.
14. A ____________________ on the old barn is loose.
15. There's a pretty bird perched on that ____________________.
16. Nobody I know gets ____________________ very often.
17. I felt ____________________ so I went out to play.
18. Ouch! I stepped on a ____________________ with a nail in it!
19. Some people are ____________________ no matter what is happening.
20. We need to nail a ____________________ over that broken window.

Name____

Date____

Break — Brake

1. Be careful not to ____________________ any dishes.
2. John was trying to repair the ____________________ on his bicycle.
3. "Hit the ____________________!" he yelled at the driver.
4. His foot was on the ____________________ but nothing was happening.
5. If you make a promise, it's important not to ____________________ it.
6. Three prisoners were secretly trying to __________________ out of jail.
7. Every ____________________ on the bus had to be replaced.
8. The boy was so angry he tried to ____________________ down the door.
9. He hit the stick on a rock in order to ____________________ it.
10. The car's emergency ____________________ is being repaired.
11. In a store, you must be careful not to ____________________ anything.
12. A ____________________ on the truck was starting to squeal.
13. Some kinds of glass are strong and hard to ____________________.
14. You were skiing so fast I was afraid you'd ____________________ a leg.
15. Drivers of covered wagons had to pull back on a stick to operate the

    ____________________.
16. The ____________________ pedal on my car is falling apart.
17. It is very difficult to ____________________ a piece of steel.
18. A karate expert can __________________ a piece of wood with his hand.
19. Be careful not to ____________________ the eggs.
20. You'd better use the ____________________ to slow down now.

Name____

Date____

Buy — By

1. How much candy did you ____________________?
2. Will you be able to do that ____________________ tomorrow?
3. We'll go ____________________ the food for the party now.
4. I went ____________________ your house last night but you weren't in.
5. She really wanted to ____________________ the dress.
6. I plan to ____________________ that radio as soon as possible.
7. Stand ____________________ the wall.
8. What should I ____________________ him for Christmas?
9. I like to shop, but I don't really like to ____________________ much.
10. This book is ____________________ Beverly Cleary.
11. A strange man walked ____________________ the window.
12. It's time to ____________________ groceries again.
13. We live ____________________ the lake.
14. Will you ____________________ me a soda, please?
15. They were marching two ____________________ two.
16. He was all ____________________ himself.
17. Someone passed ____________________ me on the street.
18. That car is nice, but it's too expensive to ____________________.
19. I was walking ____________________ your house when a car sped past.
20. I will be finished with my work ____________________ noon.

Name____

Date____

Buy — By — Bye

1. What did you ____________________ at the store?
2. We're leaving, so let's say ____________________ now.
3. We walked right ____________________ a bear without seeing it!
4. Look! The baby's waving ____________________, ____________________.
5. I don't have enough money to ____________________ this right now.
6. This book is ____________________ Scott O'Dell.
7. Say ____________________ to your grandpa, now, Jimmy!
8. They're going to ____________________ a new truck this year.
9. They said ____________________ and left in a rush.
10. Could you come ____________________ and see me today?
11. Please stand ____________________ the door and watch for the mailman.
12. I wish we didn't have to say ____________________, but we must go.
13. You just drove ____________________ the restaurant.
14. It was dark ____________________ the time they left.
15. Say ____________________ to the doggie, honey.
16. Let's ____________________ some cheese for the party.
17. It's time to say ____________________. See you later!
18. Say ____________________ to the good weather. It's starting to rain.
19. He'll have to ____________________ new tires now.
20. There's someone in your yard, ____________________ the way.

Name____

Date____

Capital — Capitol

1. Carson City is the ____________________ of Nevada.
2. The United States Congress meets in the ___________________ building.
3. Remember to start every sentence with a ____________________ letter.
4. The ____________________ of Kenya is Nairobi.
5. The meeting will be in Room 325 of the __________________ building.
6. The early Romans used only ____________________ letters.
7. The governor lives only a few blocks from the ____________________ building.
8. Some countries have more than one ____________________ city.
9. Several government offices are in the ____________________ building.
10. Brussels is sometimes called the ____________________ of Europe.
11. This word should begin with a ____________________ letter.
12. The Colorado ____________________ building has a gold dome.
13. An important word may be written in all ___________________ letters.
14. Germany’s ____________________ has moved from Bonn to Berlin.
15. Signs are usually written with ____________________ letters.
16. The ___________________ building was built more than 100 years ago.
17. There are no clear rules for using _________________ letters in poetry.
18. Most initials are written with ____________________ letters.
19. The star on the map shows the ____________________ city.
20. The ____________________ building is located south of the city center.

Name____

Date____

Ceiling — Sealing

1. The builders were ____________________ the cracks in the floor.
2. I was just ____________________ my letter.
3. The ____________________ needs to be painted again.
4. A handshake is a way of ____________________ an agreement.
5. This ____________________ looks like it might collapse.
6. The President will be ____________________ an agreement with the Mexican government tomorrow.
7. A fly was crawling across the ____________________.
8. They're redoing the kitchen ____________________.
9. The pot exploded and splattered food all over the ____________________.
10. They're ____________________ the cracks in the pavement with tar.
11. He's ____________________ off the mouse holes in the shed.
12. There's no ____________________ in the garage, just a high roof.
13. We're putting insulation in the ____________________ to save energy.
14. They're ____________________ their fate by lying.
15. The ____________________ was ruined by water.
16. This kind of tape is good for ____________________ packages.
17. Who's been ____________________ all of these empty envelopes?
18. It would be terrible if those pipes in the ____________________ froze.
19. She uses a sponge when ____________________ envelopes.
20. We cut a hole in the ____________________ for the pipe to go through.

Name____

Date____

Celery — Salary

1. I've heard that ____________________ has very few calories.
2. What is the ____________________ for this job?
3. She loves ____________________ with peanut butter.
4. The recipe calls for three sticks of ____________________.
5. He just got a raise in ____________________.
6. Lasagna wouldn't be very good without ____________________.
7. I like my job, but the ____________________ isn't too good.
8. Wages are paid by the hour. A ____________________ is usually paid by the month or year.
9. The president's ____________________ was $200,000 a year.
10. Let's put tomatoes, carrots, and ____________________ in the salad.
11. Your ____________________ for this job depends on experience.
12. This ____________________ is really stringy.
13. Creamed cheese and ____________________ make a healthy snack.
14. The boss always earns a better ____________________ than the workers.
15. The ____________________ was getting old and limp.
16. A college education usually leads to a better ____________________.
17. Her ____________________ barely covers her basic expenses.
18. I couldn't believe the grocery store was out of ____________________.
19. Many professional athletes have a very large ____________________.
20. Could you cut up some ____________________ for me?

Name____

Date____

Cell — Sell

1. She says she'll never ____________________ her house.
2. An amoeba has only one ____________________.
3. A nerve ____________________ has long tentacles.
4. They will ____________________ everything here today for half price.
5. I think I'll ____________________ my car and buy a new one.
6. Please don't ____________________ your horse.
7. Every ____________________ on the outside of your skin is dead.
8. The prisoner was locked up in a tiny ____________________.
9. I may have to ____________________ my bike to pay what I owe.
10. The hotel room was so small it seemed like a ____________________.
11. The artist wanted to ____________________ his painting for $5000.
12. She would like to ____________________ her stamp collection.
13. A single white blood ____________________ can destroy many germs.
14. The boy on the street corner has newspapers to ____________________.
15. The prisoner was pacing back and forth in his ____________________.
16. A __________________ cannot be seen without a microscope.
17. Someone lost the keys to the jail ____________________.
18. They ____________________ a lot more gas when the price goes down.
19. Her job is to ____________________ ski tickets.
20. Each red blood ____________________ needs iron to do its job.

Name____

Date____

Cent — Sent

1. I don't have a ____________________ left.
2. Have you ____________________ your letter yet?
3. Someone ____________________ roses to my mother.
4. It will cost at least a __________________ or two more to buy that brand.
5. We ____________________ them presents for Christmas.
6. I need a ____________________ more for the tax.
7. Two firemen were ____________________ to help.
8. Candy and gum used to cost just a ____________________.
9. Have they ____________________ the money yet?
10. My friend ____________________ a postcard from New York.
11. Jim is careful about every ____________________ he spends.
12. They ____________________ the book yesterday.
13. Could you lend me a ____________________?
14. She puts every ____________________ in the bank.
15. A penny is worth one ____________________.
16. I ____________________ a birthday card to my uncle.
17. Your tickets will be ____________________ in the mail.
18. The little boy needed another ____________________ to buy the candy.
19. We ____________________ the steak back because it was overdone.
20. Mark ____________________ his watch in to be fixed.

Name____

Date____

Cent — Sent — Scent

1. The air was full of the ____________________ of peppermint.
2. Mike ____________________ a letter to the editor yesterday.
3. Jane ____________________ me a copy of her newest book.
4. The boy put another ____________________ into his piggy bank.
5. The ____________________ of skunks is terrible.
6. No one knew who ____________________ the roses.
7. A stick of gum once cost only a ____________________ or two.
8. Roses have a lovely ____________________.
9. I ____________________ my Christmas presents in November.
10. It will cost only a ____________________ or two more for the best one.
11. Please call and see if they ____________________ my money back yet.
12. I love the ____________________ of frying chicken.
13. Have you ____________________ your grandma a birthday card?
14. Could you lend me a ____________________?
15. What is that funny ____________________ coming from the barn?
16. Some people are careful about every ____________________ they spend.
17. Mary Lou ____________________ a postcard from Hawaii.
18. She could smell the ____________________ of hot homemade bread.
19. The teacher ____________________ Mark to the office with a message.
20. You can't buy anything these days for just a ____________________.

Name____

Date____

Cereal — Serial

1. The first ready-to-eat ____________________ was Corn Flakes.
2. Americans eat over 20 billion bowls of ____________________ a year.
3. I'm watching a ____________________ on TV about Australia.
4. *Redbook* magazine printed the book in ____________________ form.
5. Sugared ____________________ is not especially good for you.
6. They were looking for a ____________________ killer.
7. The movie was made as a television ____________________.
8. Wheat, oats and corn are ____________________ grains.
9. Whole grain ____________________ is very nutritious.
10. The newspaper is running a ____________________ about drugs.
11. Most kinds of ____________________ have vitamins added.
12. This is the fifth episode in the ____________________.
13. He loves hot ____________________.
14. Porridge is thin ____________________.
15. The first episode was filled with suspense so that everyone would want to watch the rest of the ____________________.
16. The movie is so long it will be shown as a ____________________.
17. My favorite ____________________ is oatmeal.
18. The magazine bought ____________________ rights to the book.
19. Bran ____________________ is very healthful.
20. I like eggs and bacon better than ____________________ for breakfast.

Name______________________________________

Date______________________________________

Chews — Choose

1. Please ________________ any card you like.
2. Margie ________________ more slowly since she hurt her jaw.
3. The dog ________________ all his bones up completely.
4. We will soon have to ________________ where to go for vacation.
5. The old cow contentedly ________________ her cud.
6. Everyone please ________________ a partner for the race.
7. It can be difficult to ________________ dessert from a large menu.
8. Mike ________________ sugarless gum.
9. Let's go ________________ a Christmas tree.
10. Our rabbit looks funny when she ________________ her food.
11. I wonder if a shark ________________ his food or swallows it whole.
12. The old man got cancer because he ________________ tobacco.
13. You must ________________ your friends carefully.
14. Did you ________________ an ice cream flavor yet?
15. A beaver ________________ down tree after tree to build its den.
16. Everyone must ________________ a number between one and fifty.
17. The mouse just ________________ a new hole every time we plug up the old one.
18. We each ________________ between right and wrong every day.
19. A tire chain ________________ up the tire as well as the road.
20. It's time to ________________ teams for the baseball game.

Name____

Date____

Clothes — Close

1. I need to wash my ____________________ today.
2. Would you please ____________________ the door?
3. Please ____________________ the drawers before you leave the room.
4. There is a sale on ____________________ at the mall this weekend.
5. The pilot forgot to ____________________ his flight plan.
6. These are the only ____________________ I brought with me.
7. Your new ____________________ look great on you.
8. Be sure to ____________________ the cupboards when you're finished or your sister might bump her head.
9. The closet was packed with ____________________.
10. Please ____________________ your books and listen to the teacher.
11. She had so many ____________________ in her suitcase it wouldn't shut.
12. For a better vacation, take fewer _________________ and more money.
13. My ____________________ are all wrinkled!
14. Would someone please ____________________ the window?
15. School will ____________________ for the summer on June 10.
16. We need to _________________ the curtains before watching the movie.
17. She can wear her mother's ____________________ already.
18. It is good manners to __________________ your mouth while chewing.
19. I'll give you a surprise if you ____________________ your eyes.
20. We gave some of our old ____________________ to charity.

Name____

Date____

Conscience — Conscious

1. The injured man was still ____________________.
2. His ____________________ told him it would be wrong to lie.
3. Most of the brain's work is below the ____________________ level.
4. It would be a better world if everyone heeded their ________________.
5. The patient was no longer ____________________.
6. Everyone has an inner voice called a ____________________.
7. He became ____________________ of a pain in his side.
8. She was concentrating so hard on her work that she was not ____________________ of anything else around her.
9. People who ignore their ____________________ get into trouble.
10. He doesn't seem to be bothered at all by his ____________________.
11. Maybe he's ____________________ but just resting.
12. He was ____________________ of someone watching him.
13. She was ____________________ of a drop in temperature.
14. Some criminals seem to have no ____________________.
15. I was ____________________ throughout the operation.
16. Your ____________________ can make you feel guilty for doing wrong.
17. The sick person was barely ____________________.
18. Do animals have a ____________________?
19. The ____________________ leads people to do heroic things sometimes.
20. Your ____________________ can bother you even if no one else knows.

Name____

Date____

Council — Counsel

1. His job is to ___________________ people who need jobs.
2. The student ___________________ is planning a talent show.
3. A special ___________________ was set up to study the problem.
4. Lawyers give legal ___________________.
5. The ___________________ finally approved our budget.
6. She was hired to ___________________ the students about careers.
7. The nurse can ___________________ children who have problems.
8. He needed someone to ___________________ him about his problem.
9. The ___________________ will meet January 17.
10. Everyone on the city ___________________ was in agreement.
11. She charges $100 an hour to ___________________ people.
12. Could you tell me where the student ___________________ is meeting?
13. No one can ___________________ you on this. The decision is yours.
14. I was trying to ___________________ my friend.
15. He was elected to the ___________________ in 2005.
16. She will ___________________ you about how to stay out of trouble.
17. The city ___________________ wanted to fire the mayor.
18. There were five people on the ___________________.
19. Her mother was always willing to ___________________ her daughter.
20. Everyone's invited to the ___________________ meeting.

Name____

Date____

Course — Coarse

1. Hundreds of fans were at the race ________________.
2. The sandpaper was very ________________.
3. The bulldog had ________________, wiry hair.
4. She really likes her history ________________.
5. I'm not sure which is the best ________________ to take from here.
6. I ran through the ________________ grass and hurt my feet.
7. The obstacle ________________ is harder than last year's.
8. The hard work made her hands feel ________________.
9. The plane's ________________ was toward New York.
10. The wood was very ________________.
11. The girl took a wrong turn and ran off of the ________________.
12. The cat's fur was ________________ with dried mud.
13. The driver raced around the ________________.
14. I took a math ________________ in college.
15. My father bought ________________ sandpaper to start the project.
16. The bread was made with ________________ flour.
17. The airplane was diverted from its ________________ by a bad storm.
18. Of ________________ I expect you to win!
19. Canvas is a ________________ fabric.
20. I think you're the best, of ________________.

Name____

Date____

Creak — Creek

1. A lot of fish were in the ____________________.
2. A bike path ran along the ____________________.
3. He heard something ____________________ in the shadows.
4. The shutters began to ____________________ in the wind.
5. The stairs ____________________ even if you tiptoe.
6. There was very little water in the ____________________ that summer.
7. Whenever the wind blew, things would ____________________.
8. Look, there's an animal at the ____________________.
9. There's a beautiful waterfall on this ____________________.
10. The old trees ____________________ in the breeze.
11. I want a nice cabin on a little ____________________ somewhere.
12. This ____________________ flows into the Rio Grande River.
13. It's not safe to drink from that ____________________.
14. Some oil should fix that ____________________ in the door.
15. Two of my cupboard doors ____________________.
16. A grizzly bear has been fishing in this ____________________.
17. The jewels were kept in a trunk that would ____________________ when it was opened.
18. It was difficult to get through the bushes to the ____________________.
19. I remember the ____________________ of Grandma's old rocking chair.
20. My old bones are beginning to ____________________.

Name____

Date____

Dear — Deer

1. The men were hunting for ____________________.
2. "____________________ Jane," she wrote as she began her letter.
3. "Thank you, ____________________," said the old woman.
4. We saw a lot of ____________________ in the forest.
5. My ____________________ friend Sandra is traveling in Mexico now.
6. "She is such a ____________________ little girl," bragged Mary's grandmother.
7. Letters usually start with the word "____________________."
8. A ____________________ can easily jump over a fence.
9. Drivers must be careful not to hit any ____________________.
10. Could you do me a favor, ____________________?
11. "____________________ Mother," the note began.
12. A female ____________________ is called a doe.
13. Two or three ____________________ were grazing in the field.
14. My ____________________ grandmother died two years ago.
15. The headlights lit up the eyes of the ____________________.
16. "____________________ me," fretted the old woman.
17. Oh ____________________! I am so sorry.
18. A herd of ____________________ fled up the hillside.
19. A baby ____________________ is covered with spots.
20. The sign says to watch for ____________________.

Name____

Date____

Desert — Dessert

1. We had vanilla ice cream for ____________________.
2. He was stranded in the middle of the ____________________.
3. The ____________________ was sweet and very filling.
4. The temperature in the ____________________ can be over 100° F.
5. We felt sure he would never ____________________ us.
6. Last night we had a three-layer cake for ____________________.
7. He was lost in the ____________________ without food or water.
8. I want banana cream pie for ____________________.
9. I had two helpings of ____________________.
10. A good friend will never ____________________ his companions.
11. He wandered alone in the ____________________ for several days.
12. We were served banana splits for ____________________.
13. It can be dangerous if your car breaks down in the ____________________.
14. Cheesecake is my favorite ____________________.
15. Join us for ____________________ at about 7:00 this evening.
16. It took many days to walk across the ____________________.
17. Soldiers who ____________________ their unit will be punished.
18. I thought the ____________________ was too sweet and sticky.
19. We almost never eat ____________________.
20. If it rains, the plants in the ____________________ might bloom.

Name____

Date____

Dew — Do — Due

1. They ____________________ not know what's happening.
2. What did you ____________________ yesterday?
3. The grass was covered with ____________________.
4. You can ____________________ almost anything if you work hard.
5. Your payment is ____________________ March 13.
6. The spider web sparkled with ____________________.
7. I don't understand how they ____________________ that.
8. This library book was ____________________ a week ago!
9. Is there anything I can ____________________ to help?
10. The money for the pictures is ____________________ when they come.
11. The car window was covered with ____________________.
12. I have a lot to ____________________ today.
13. The lunch money is ____________________ at the beginning of the day.
14. I love you and I'd never ____________________ anything to hurt you.
15. The bright sun evaporated the ____________________ from the leaves.
16. It's the truth. I really didn't ____________________ it.
17. Your homework is ____________________ before class begins.
18. The morning was fresh with ____________________.
19. What did the cat ____________________ this time?
20. They don't know when their money is ____________________.

Name____

Date____

Die — Dye

1. She was afraid her dog would ________________ if he ran in the street.
2. It was so funny he thought he'd ____________________ laughing.
3. The cloth had been colored with purple ____________________.
4. People can ____________________ if a tornado hits their house.
5. She asked the hairdresser to cut her hair and ____________________ it.
6. More wild animals ____________________ in winter than in summer.
7. He planned to ____________________ his coat.
8. The ____________________ faded when the dress was washed.
9. Long ago, dandelions were used to make ____________________.
10. That old tree in the yard looks like it's going to ___________________.
11. The mountain climbers knew they could ____________________ if they weren't careful.
12. I need to buy some ____________________ for the Easter eggs.
13. Food is often colored with special ____________________.
14. The doctor was sure his patient would not ____________________.
15. Chemical ____________________ can cause pollution.
16. She was so embarrassed she thought she would ____________________.
17. The baby birds might ____________________ if the weather turns cold.
18. Let's ____________________ this tablecloth a different color.
19. When her hair turned gray, she started to ____________________ it.
20. No one will ever ____________________ because of a broken fingernail!

Name____

Date____

Fair — Fare

1. The ____________________ has just been raised to $1.00.
2. The judge is trying to be ____________________ to everyone.
3. "That's not ____________________!" shouted the batter.
4. I'm sorry. You must have exact change for the ____________________.
5. No one can be perfectly ____________________ all of the time.
6. We did a ____________________ job on the project.
7. Everyone needs to bring 50¢ for the bus ____________________.
8. There will be a book ____________________ next week at school.
9. They charge a special low ____________________ for senior citizens.
10. A conductor came around to collect my ____________________.
11. These laws are supposed to be ____________________ to everyone.
12. He thinks anything that doesn't go his way isn't ____________________.
13. I would take the train, but the ____________________ is too high.
14. A long time ago, the bus ____________________ was only a nickel.
15. Life is not ____________________!
16. Not everyone thought the umpire made a ____________________ call.
17. It didn't seem ____________________ that some people had plenty of money while others didn't have enough food.
18. They're in a freight car because they couldn't pay the ________________.
19. That man isn't even trying to be ____________________!
20. Please drop the ____________________ into the machine.

Name____

Date____

Fir — Fur

1. She loves to stroke the cat's soft ____________________.
2. Many homes are built with ____________________.
3. Nearly all of the ____________________ trees here have died.
4. The woman wore an expensive ____________________ coat.
5. Would you rather your Christmas tree be spruce or ________________?
6. The Douglas ____________________ has beautiful cones.
7. A sea otter must constantly clean its ____________________.
8. The dog is shedding its coat of winter ____________________.
9. Plywood may be made from ____________________.
10. The slippers were lined with soft ____________________.
11. Reindeer ____________________ is hollow, to provide insulation.
12. Many people in Russia wear ____________________ caps.
13. We climbed the old ____________________ tree this morning.
14. A beautiful ____________________ hung on the wall of the old lodge.
15. Mange is a disease which causes a dog's _________________ to fall out.
16. He told me that ____________________ is a strong wood with few knots.
17. It looks as if a porcupine has been eating the __________________ tree.
18. Some of the bear's shaggy ________________ was hanging on a bush.
19. It is illegal to buy ____________________ from endangered animals.
20. The ____________________ of certain seals is used by the Eskimos to make mukluks.

Name____

Date____

Flew — Flu

1. I wasn't in school yesterday because I had the __________________.
2. The airplane __________________ faster than the speed of sound.
3. All of the ducks __________________ south in the fall.
4. Winter is the __________________ season.
5. The arrow __________________ straight through the air.
6. Have you ever had the stomach __________________?
7. The jet __________________ directly north.
8. I hope you don't catch the __________________.
9. Have you had a __________________ shot yet?
10. A bird __________________ into the window.
11. Mike __________________ his small plane over the pass.
12. A wasp __________________ into the car.
13. He got the __________________ and missed the concert.
14. I'm not sure if they drove or __________________.
15. We __________________ to Mexico for our vacation.
16. The __________________ is caused by a virus, not a germ.
17. Many people used to die from the __________________.
18. The helicopter __________________ close to the ground.
19. My paper airplane __________________ farther than the others.
20. She was in bed all day with the __________________.

Name____

Date____

Flour — Flower

1. The rose is a beautiful ____________________!
2. Bread is made with ____________________, water and yeast.
3. The state ____________________ of Nebraska is the goldenrod.
4. I brought my mother a pretty ____________________.
5. Every ____________________ but one was yellow.
6. Gravy is often thickened with ____________________.
7. We ground the wheat into ____________________.
8. Please water this ____________________ twice a week.
9. Something had chewed a hole in the ____________________ sack.
10. He put too much ____________________ in the pancakes.
11. The first ____________________ bloomed in April.
12. She wore a small ____________________ in her hair.
13. At some air shows, pilots drop bombs filled with ____________________ on targets.
14. Almost every ____________________ in the highest mountains is small.
15. Did you know that ____________________ is bleached to make it white?
16. Shortening and ____________________ are mixed to make pie crusts.
17. The recipe calls for four cups of ____________________.
18. The carnation is her favorite ____________________.
19. Is that a real ____________________ or is it silk?
20. The chicken was coated with ____________________ and then fried.

Name____

Date____

For — Four

1. My brother is ____________________ years old.
2. This gift is ____________________ you.
3. I only have ____________________ cents.
4. They need new rugs ____________________ their house.
5. Jan does everything ____________________ her sister.
6. Can you stand very still ____________________ three minutes?
7. It's only ____________________ days until Christmas.
8. Will you throw this away ____________________ me?
9. I have ____________________ good friends.
10. The prize is ____________________ the winner.
11. I am making something ____________________ my mom.
12. Do you have ____________________ pencils?
13. Mark has ____________________ sisters.
14. What did you get ____________________ your birthday?
15. All of this wood is ____________________ the fireplace.
16. It is too cold ____________________ outside recess.
17. Only three or ____________________ of you can come.
18. Here is a box ____________________ your toys.
19. Mrs. Smith needs ____________________ helpers.
20. One of these letters is ____________________ you.

Name____

Date____

Form — From

1. They drove ____________________ New York to Florida last summer.
2. This dress is ____________________ Greece.
3. Did you use the correct ____________________ for your letter?
4. I got a book ____________________ my grandmother yesterday.
5. What ____________________ of address should I use?
6. Sedimentary rocks ____________________ because of heat and pressure.
7. Where are those people ____________________?
8. Ice will ____________________ near the shore first.
9. The airplane came ____________________ the west.
10. We got a letter ____________________ the President!
11. Please ____________________ a single line.
12. We'll ____________________ the dough into shapes now.
13. Much of our sugar comes ____________________ Hawaii.
14. Drifted snow can ____________________ strange shapes.
15. Water changes ____________________ liquid to ice at 32° F.
16. Dripping water in cold weather will ____________________ icicles.
17. Democracy is our ____________________ of government.
18. His luck went ____________________ bad to worse.
19. You must correctly fill out the ____________________ in order to get a refund.
20. I had a phone call ____________________ a long-lost friend today.

Name____

Date____

Forth — Fourth

1. My sister's in the ____________________ grade this year.
2. Go ____________________, young man!
3. The curtains were swinging back and ____________________.
4. The ____________________ place winner gets $50.00.
5. This is the ____________________ time I've spoken to you about this!
6. Would Mr. Jacobs please step ____________________?
7. It took courage for the pioneers to go ____________________ into the wilderness.
8. You're the ____________________ person who's called about this!
9. His office is the ____________________ door to the left.
10. This is the ____________________ fish I've caught today!
11. The lion was pacing back and ____________________ in his cage.
12. School ended on the ____________________ of June that year.
13. The ____________________ caller will win a $25.00 gift certificate.
14. We were ____________________ in line for tickets.
15. She has the ability to go ____________________ and meet any challenge.
16. The ____________________ problem on the page is the most difficult.
17. We were driving back and ____________________ for hours.
18. The ____________________ time I wrote to them they finally answered.
19. She's in her ____________________ year of college.
20. Please send this package by ____________________ class mail.

Name____

Date____

Great — Grate

1. What a ____________________ idea!
2. Would you ____________________ this cheese for me?
3. That is a ____________________ big building!
4. George Washington was a ____________________ man.
5. We need to ____________________ some lemon peel.
6. She's a ____________________ cook!
7. I think I'll ____________________ the garlic now.
8. Hawaii is a ____________________ place to go for a winter vacation.
9. What a ____________________ day!
10. I'm having trouble cleaning the ____________________.
11. I didn't think the movie was that ____________________.
12. Sir Isaac Newton was a ____________________ scientist.
13. You did a ____________________ job on your paper!
14. A storm ____________________ covered the end of the pipe.
15. I had a ____________________ time at the party!
16. It felt ____________________ to be in first place!
17. I think you're ____________________!
18. Now I'll ____________________ some cabbage for coleslaw.
19. Hank Aaron was ____________________ at hitting home runs.
20. The noise began to ____________________ on his nerves.

Name____

Date____

Groan — Grown

1. These flowers were ____________________ in a hothouse.
2. The baby has ____________________ a lot in the last six months.
3. The poor dog let out a long ____________________.
4. The bushes have finally ____________________ tall enough to cover the entrance of the cave.
5. I heard him ____________________ when his coat ripped.
6. My nephew is a ____________________ man now.
7. There was a ____________________ from the crowd.
8. He started to ____________________ in his sleep.
9. Something in the forest made a loud ____________________.
10. She has ____________________ her own vegetables for many years.
11. They decided to adopt a fully ____________________ dog as a pet.
12. Whatever you do, don't ____________________, even if you're unhappy.
13. I haven't seen her in a long time. She's ____________________ old.
14. The home ____________________ vegetables were delicious.
15. Weeds have ____________________ up all through the yard and garden.
16. His broken ankle hurt so much he had to ____________________.
17. I was so discouraged I just wanted to ____________________.
18. Things have ____________________ worse over time.
19. Don't moan and ____________________ about everything!
20. I heard the wounded animal ____________________ in pain.

Name____

Date____

Guessed — Guest

1. I didn't know the answer, so I ____________________.
2. He ____________________ my name correctly.
3. We will be having a ____________________ for dinner.
4. May I introduce you to our ____________________ from Japan?
5. Please be my ____________________.
6. Who ____________________ the number of beans in the jar?
7. I'm afraid our ____________________ may have left her coat.
8. We ____________________ that you would be here.
9. He ____________________ correctly that the weather would change.
10. He showed the ____________________ to his room.
11. She ____________________ that she was going in the right direction.
12. The audience ____________________ the outcome of the play.
13. The principal will be our ____________________ today.
14. Would you be my ____________________ tonight?
15. No one ____________________ how bad the injury was.
16. We heard a howl in the distance and __________________ it was a wolf.
17. I think she is Carol's ____________________ this weekend.
18. A ____________________ should always thank the hostess with a note.
19. He ____________________ that his parents might be upset when they heard his story.
20. Our ____________________ will arrive early tomorrow morning.

Name____

Date____

Hair — Hare

1. The actress had long shiny ____________________.
2. I can't believe how much ____________________ that dog sheds!
3. It's sometimes hard to tell a rabbit from a ____________________.
4. Your ____________________ looks great today!
5. Why does ____________________ turn gray when people get old?
6. A tuft of animal ____________________ was hanging on the bush.
7. A fox chased the ____________________ back into its hole.
8. We could see the tracks of a ____________________ in the snow.
9. I need to get my ____________________ cut.
10. There is a great story about a tortoise and a ____________________.
11. Her ____________________ is naturally curly.
12. All mammals, even whales, have ____________________.
13. We have rabbits here, but I've never seen a ____________________.
14. Some animals have ____________________ all over their bodies.
15. It's a good idea to tie back your ____________________ while cooking.
16. The trapper brought back a ____________________ for dinner.
17. Sometimes a ____________________ can outsmart a dog.
18. His ____________________ and clothes were dripping wet.
19. An eagle swooped down on the ____________________.
20. The baby's ____________________ is so soft!

Name____

Date____

Hall — Haul

1. Let's talk for a moment out in the ____________________.
2. My truck can ____________________ a full load of gravel.
3. Our room is at the end of the ____________________.
4. His picture is in a ____________________ of fame.
5. We'll use the trailer to ____________________ the trash to the dump.
6. The class lined up in the ____________________.
7. The dinner was to be held in a large meeting ____________________.
8. Trucks are used to ____________________ much of America's freight.
9. We'll use a sled to ____________________ the food to the cabin.
10. The community ____________________ is a good place to hold the dance.
11. The van can ____________________ twelve people and their things.
12. The office is just down the ____________________.
13. How will we ____________________ the building materials to the lot?
14. The city will soon ____________________ away recyclable items.
15. This is too much to ____________________ in one load.
16. The town ____________________ was crowded for the meeting.
17. The ____________________ will be waxed during spring vacation.
18. We couldn't ____________________ everything in our little car.
19. Our teacher was supposed to decorate the ____________________.
20. I will ____________________ away your old newspapers.

Name____

Date____

Hay — Hey

1. We need to buy ____________________ for the horses.
2. ____________________ you! Can you help me?
3. It is fun to play in the ____________________.
4. ____________________! What are you doing?
5. ____________________ John! Are you in there?
6. I think there are mice in the ____________________.
7. The policeman shouted, "____________________, thief!"
8. The ____________________ was ready to be cut.
9. The tractor had a big load of ____________________.
10. He heard an echo when he shouted, "____________________!"
11. The barn was full of ____________________.
12. ____________________ Mr. Green! May we go with you?
13. Cows like green grass better than ____________________.
14. The farmer was afraid the rain would ruin his ____________________.
15. ____________________ is dried grass.
16. ____________________! Stop that!
17. A bale of ____________________ fell off of the truck.
18. The rancher had all the ____________________ he needed for winter.
19. ____________________! Be careful!
20. ____________________! Don't touch that door!

Name____

Date____

Heal — Heel

1. It takes a long time for a broken bone to ________________.
2. The shopping cart hit my ________________ and it hurt!
3. Crying can sometimes help ________________ hurt feelings.
4. A scab has to form for a cut to ________________.
5. In this dance, you touch your toe, then your ________________.
6. A person's eyes usually ________________ quickly if they're hurt.
7. I'm not sure my back will ever ________________.
8. You will ________________ much faster if you rest.
9. I want shoes with an open ________________.
10. The ________________ of my boot is falling off.
11. He stepped on a nail and hurt his ________________.
12. Some people think time will ________________ all wounds.
13. The little boy kicked the ball with his ________________.
14. The doctor says your arm will ________________ within a month.
15. A dog bit that little girl's ________________.
16. Her wrist was crushed so badly it will never ________________.
17. Dogs lick their wounds because it helps them ________________.
18. That shoe has such a high ________________ I don't know how anyone could wear it.
19. The ________________ of the sock was bright red.
20. Bad burns ________________ slowly.

Name____

Date____

Hear — Here

1. Did you ____________________ about the terrible snowstorm?
2. Could you say that again! I didn't ____________________ you.
3. Would you come ____________________ for a moment?
4. I can ____________________ the faintest sounds at night.
5. The animals will come over ____________________ if I call them.
6. The judge asked, "Is everyone ____________________?"
7. Look, your ball is over ____________________!
8. He could almost ____________________ the bear breathing.
9. I am right ____________________! Come and get me!
10. I can ____________________ singing. Can you?
11. The old man can't ____________________ too well anymore.
12. The lady could ____________________ someone screaming.
13. The house is supposed to be around ____________________ somewhere.
14. Didn't you ____________________ me calling?
15. We live right ____________________.
16. My brother was ____________________ a minute ago.
17. I saw a snake right ____________________ yesterday.
18. It was so noisy I couldn't ____________________ what she was saying.
19. I've always wanted to come ____________________ for vacation.
20. My coat must be in ____________________ someplace!

Name____

Date____

Heard — Herd

1. We saw a ____________________ of reindeer.
2. Quiet! I think I ____________________ something!
3. He ____________________ a strange noise in the night.
4. Nobody has ____________________ anything about it yet.
5. The rancher owned a large ____________________ of cattle.
6. We ____________________ a wolf howling in the distance.
7. The cowboys began to ____________________ the horses into the corral.
8. Have you ____________________ the news?
9. No one has ____________________ from her for three months.
10. A ____________________ of deer was in the field.
11. The buffalo ____________________ began to stampede.
12. The dog’s barking. He must have ____________________ something.
13. Elephants generally travel together in a ____________________ led by an old female.
14. We walked very quietly, but the animals ____________________ us.
15. A group of birds isn’t a ____________________, it’s a flock.
16. They ____________________ what sounded like a gun.
17. Have you ____________________ about the sale here tomorrow?
18. A ____________________ of sheep was grazing on the hillside.
19. The sea lions around here are all from the same ____________________.
20. He ____________________ the airplane before he saw it.

Name____

Date____

Higher — Hire

1. I hope the telephone company will __________________ me.
2. Mt. Everest is a lot __________________ than Mt. McKinley.
3. We cannot __________________ anyone without a college degree.
4. The restaurant needs to __________________ two new waitresses.
5. I can jump __________________ than you!
6. Jets can fly a lot __________________ than small planes.
7. There is less oxygen at __________________ elevations.
8. It is likely that they will __________________ me soon.
9. Your work is so good I want to __________________ you permanently.
10. I don’t think we should climb any __________________ today.
11. We want to __________________ someone to remodel the kitchen.
12. This ladder will reach a lot __________________ than the others.
13. You can reach __________________ than me, can’t you?
14. It is impossible for us to __________________ anyone at this time.
15. We watched the balloon float __________________ and __________________ into the sky until it disappeared.
16. We plan to __________________ a teenager to care for the lawn.
17. These buildings are __________________ than any I’ve seen before.
18. These prices are a lot __________________ than they were last week.
19. I’d love to help, but you’ll need to __________________ me.
20. The wages for this job are __________________ than for my last job.

Name____

Date____

Hole — Whole

1. Does the ____________________ world know about this?
2. I haven't seen him for a ____________________ month.
3. The men dug a big ____________________ to trap the animal.
4. Did you eat the ____________________ thing?
5. The treasure was buried in a deep ____________________.
6. A ____________________ bunch of kids are in the park.
7. The dog has his nose down the rabbit ____________________.
8. A little mouse peeked out of his ____________________.
9. There is a big ____________________ in my shirt!
10. The ____________________ school was cheering.
11. Tim ate a ____________________ box of ice cream.
12. I did the ____________________ job myself.
13. The boys came in through a ____________________ in the fence.
14. You're a ____________________ hour early.
15. A squirrel family lives in a ____________________ in that tree.
16. Can you eat a ____________________ watermelon?
17. The man drilled a ____________________ in the end of the board.
18. Would you please plug that ____________________ for me?
19. Mary dug a little ____________________ for each plant.
20. The ____________________ building was on fire.

Name____

Date____

Horse — Hoarse

1. Mary has wanted a ____________________ since she was five.
2. My voice is still ____________________ from shouting at the game.
3. I'm sorry I'm so ____________________. I have a cold.
4. You're so ____________________ I can barely understand you.
5. Can you ride a ____________________?
6. Their ____________________ was loose last week.
7. His voice is naturally ____________________.
8. Let's go saddle the ____________________.
9. Which ____________________ do you think can run the fastest?
10. A hundred years ago, the ____________________ was more important than the automobile.
11. My dog has a ____________________ bark.
12. She rides her ____________________ every morning before school.
13. The raven has a ____________________ call.
14. Don't scream or you'll be too ____________________ to talk tomorrow.
15. Which ____________________ would you like?
16. I heard a ____________________ sound coming from the woods.
17. The ____________________ was pulling a small cart.
18. After two days of hard travel, the ____________________ was exhausted.
19. I heard a ____________________ voice answer the phone.
20. After her tonsils were removed, she was a bit ____________________.

Name____

Date____

Hour — Our

1. We need to leave in one ____________________.
2. This is ____________________ classroom.
3. It happened about an ____________________ ago.
4. It is an ____________________ later than I thought.
5. I wonder if ____________________ parents are here yet.
6. It is ____________________ job to do the dishes.
7. Would you like ____________________ phone number?
8. We start a new class every ____________________.
9. That picture shows ____________________ family.
10. It is only an ____________________ until sundown.
11. The boy went to get ____________________ mail.
12. We thought ____________________ house was burning.
13. That clock is an ____________________ slow.
14. The workmen will paint ____________________ shed next week.
15. I will meet you in an ____________________.
16. It will take about an ____________________ to do all these dishes.
17. The baby sleeps for an ____________________ or more every afternoon.
18. We will sing ____________________ favorite song for you.
19. We have to ask ____________________ mother.
20. The sun will set in less than one ____________________.

Name____

Date____

I — Eye

1. Be careful not to hurt your ____________________.
2. ____________________ want to learn to draw.
3. Jane and ____________________ are best friends.
4. ____________________ can't understand what you said.
5. Keep your ____________________ on the ball.
6. Do you think ____________________ can help?
7. He is blind in one ____________________.
8. ____________________ called you last week.
9. His ____________________ is red.
10. My brother had something in his ____________________.
11. Looking at the sun can hurt your ____________________.
12. My mom and ____________________ are cleaning house.
13. Does the doctor know ____________________ am here?
14. He is going to look at my ____________________.
15. ____________________ don't like cats.
16. Will you ask if ____________________ can be next?
17. Close your right ____________________.
18. ____________________ will do my best.
19. He fell down and hurt his ____________________.
20. The man had a black ____________________.

Name____

Date____

Its — It's

1. It looks like ____________________ raining again.
2. She was very pleased with ____________________ color.
3. ____________________ fur was brown and white.
4. ____________________ a beautiful, sunny day!
5. After several months, ____________________ leg finally healed.
6. ____________________ not fair!
7. Can you tell me if ____________________ working?
8. ____________________ windows were broken.
9. I can't tell if ____________________ hot or cold.
10. I think ____________________ going to be an exciting day.
11. A dog sheds ____________________ coat at least once a year.
12. ____________________ even bigger than the last fish I caught!
13. When the book fell in the snow, ____________________ cover was ruined.
14. I'm afraid ____________________ going to be a long day.
15. ____________________ good to be home.
16. ____________________ fur was long and very soft.
17. I think ____________________ the best ice cream!
18. ____________________ collar is gold plated.
19. Mother says ____________________ too dark to play outside.
20. ____________________ name is Big Blue.

Name____

Date____

Lead — Led

1. An old Indian ____________________ the way through the wilderness.
2. Bullets are made of ____________________.
3. Did you know that ____________________ is heavier than gold?
4. People can get sick and even die from ____________________ poisoning.
5. The guide ____________________ them safely to the top of the pass.
6. Sailboats have ____________________ in the keel to keep them from tipping over.
7. The dog ____________________ his master to the wrecked plane.
8. No one ____________________ us here. We found the way ourselves.
9. People have used ____________________ for thousands of years.
10. Coach Brown ____________________ the team to a third straight win.
11. Divers carry ____________________ weights to keep them underwater.
12. She was so tired her feet felt like ____________________.
13. The trail ____________________ us right to the cabin.
14. I'm afraid we've been ____________________ in the wrong direction.
15. Wow! This feels like it's made of ____________________.
16. We attached two small ____________________ weights to the fishing line.
17. The park ranger ____________________ a nature walk each morning.
18. A dirt road ____________________ us into the mountains.
19. The music director ____________________ the audience in song.
20. The pencil ____________________ broke again and again.

Name____

Date____

Loose — Lose

1. My belt is ____________________. I'd better tighten it.
2. Be careful not to ____________________ your wallet.
3. Why is it I always ____________________ my favorite toys?
4. My tooth is ____________________. I should have it pulled.
5. Our dog likes to break his rope and run ____________________.
6. I'm really afraid that our team is going to ____________________.
7. A ____________________ string was hanging from the ceiling.
8. His coat seems ____________________ since he lost weight.
9. You have nothing to ____________________ by trying this.
10. If you don't work hard, you might ____________________ your job.
11. It makes me angry when I ____________________ my keys.
12. The horses were running ____________________ in the field.
13. His desk was cluttered with ____________________ papers.
14. Most people would much rather win than ____________________.
15. It's best not to have ____________________ papers in your notebook.
16. If you are not careful, you'll ____________________ something.
17. You will ____________________ too much sleep if you stay up for the movie.
18. Your shoelace seems to be ____________________.
19. Be careful not to ____________________ your lunch money.
20. Oh no! The rope has come ____________________.

Name____

Date____

Maid — Made

1. Dennis ____________________ a cake for his wife's birthday.
2. People ____________________ their own butter years ago.
3. The ____________________ did all of the shopping and cleaning.
4. He worked hard and ____________________ a lot of money last year.
5. I'm afraid the ____________________ may have stolen some silverware.
6. He ____________________ me do it!
7. She got a job as a ____________________ at the hotel.
8. He ____________________ himself finish his work.
9. This sweater was ____________________ in New Zealand.
10. The ____________________ is talking with the butler.
11. The ____________________ comes here on Thursdays.
12. A strong wind ____________________ the house shudder.
13. The story ____________________ no sense to me.
14. The animal ____________________ a very strange sound.
15. Our ____________________ is a wonderful cook!
16. Janet's mother ____________________ her practice the piano daily.
17. The gardener married the ____________________.
18. My grandmother ____________________ this hat for me.
19. She ____________________ sandwiches for lunch.
20. The ____________________ is ready to clean the room.

Name____

Date____

Mail — Male

1. A __________________ moose is called a bull.
2. The check is in the __________________.
3. The __________________ plane was late.
4. A __________________ born in the U.S. can expect to live 71 years.
5. I need to get to the Post Office to __________________ my letter.
6. Be sure to __________________ in your reservation.
7. In the 1960s it cost only 5¢ to __________________ a letter.
8. Usually __________________ cats are extremely independent.
9. The fish I caught was a __________________.
10. I get a lot of things in the __________________ from my pen pal.
11. Birds with very bright colors are usually __________________.
12. Only __________________ animals may be hunted in this area.
13. Four of the puppies are __________________.
14. I ordered these shoes from a __________________ order catalog.
15. Someone once sent enough cinder blocks to build a house through the __________________!
16. Most __________________ animals are larger than the females.
17. We haven't had any __________________ for several days.
18. The Post Office will hold your __________________ if you're gone.
19. More __________________ babies are born than female.
20. It's against the law to steal someone's __________________.

Name____

Date____

Main — Mane

1. The ____________________ reason they moved was to be near their relatives.
2. Female lions do not have a ____________________.
3. The girl gently brushed her horse's ____________________.
4. Is this really the ____________________ road?
5. My ____________________ job is working with computers.
6. Its ____________________ was braided and decorated with ribbons.
7. Many years ago, people ate their ____________________ meal at noon.
8. When you read, it's important to understand the ________________ idea.
9. The ____________________ thing is not to give up too soon.
10. The visitors were standing near the ____________________ entrance.
11. If you start to fall off of a horse, hold on to its ____________________.
12. The ____________________ power source has gone out.
13. The animal's ____________________ was so long it had to be cut.
14. I'm sorry, but this isn't the ____________________ airport.
15. The race will be the ____________________ event today.
16. The girl drew a pink and green zebra with a blue ____________________.
17. We'll ski down the ____________________ trail this time.
18. The lion shook its ____________________ and growled.
19. The little donkey had sticks tangled in its ____________________.
20. I'll meet you in the ____________________ lodge at noon.

Name____

Date____

Meat — Meet

1. I would love to ____________________ your friends.
2. They say ____________________ is a good source of protein.
3. They agreed to ____________________ after school.
4. You never know who you might ____________________ at the store.
5. Wolves must eat a lot of ____________________ to live.
6. The ____________________ market was closed on Sundays.
7. Vegetarians don't eat any ____________________.
8. We're going to ____________________ our guests at the airport tonight.
9. I was hoping to ____________________ the boss here.
10. The ____________________ was beginning to spoil.
11. My dog likes cheese and ____________________.
12. I'd like you to ____________________ my mother.
13. She loves to ____________________ new people.
14. Some little animal has been stealing our ____________________.
15. We'll never be able to eat all of that ____________________!
16. The school track ____________________ is on Saturday.
17. Please ____________________ me at the bridge.
18. The ____________________ was undercooked.
19. This ____________________ should be ground up into hamburger.
20. The ____________________ had a lot of fat on it.

Name____

Date____

Missed — Mist

1. A soft __________________ rose from the lake.
2. We all __________________ you when you were gone.
3. I'm sorry I __________________ your call.
4. Drops fell from the trees as I walked through the __________________.
5. They just __________________ the train.
6. I'm sorry I'm late. I __________________ the bus this morning.
7. A heavy __________________ rose from the river, coating the trees with frost.
8. Oh no! I __________________ my appointment today.
9. The batter __________________ the ball.
10. I __________________ the first three questions on the test.
11. The __________________ softened our voices and footsteps.
12. Everything looked different in the __________________.
13. The arrow __________________ the target altogether.
14. The sun burned away the morning __________________.
15. The little cabin was hidden in the __________________.
16. The carpenter __________________ the nail and hit his finger.
17. I could see a herd of deer through the __________________.
18. Oh no! I think we __________________ the turnoff.
19. The forest seemed more frightening than ever in the __________________.
20. A cold gray __________________ rose from the sea.

Name____

Date____

New — Knew

1. He ____________________ about the contest, but he didn't enter.
2. Please get me a ____________________ rubber band from the drawer.
3. My dad is wearing his ____________________ shirt.
4. They bought me a ____________________ bike for my birthday.
5. I ____________________ him when he was young.
6. Her brand ____________________ doll was broken.
7. He thought he ____________________ everyone there.
8. Nobody ____________________ what had happened.
9. She ____________________ she had left her diamonds in the safe.
10. Their ____________________ house is much larger than the old one.
11. My family bought a brand ____________________ car yesterday.
12. She ____________________ that he was going to try to trick her.
13. Everybody ____________________ something strange was going on.
14. It is upsetting when something __________________ breaks right away.
15. No one ____________________ that he had once been in prison.
16. There's a ____________________ student in our class.
17. I think he ____________________ about this all along.
18. It is great to buy ____________________ clothes.
19. I ____________________ you would like each other.
20. She ____________________ there was going to be trouble.

Name____

Date____

Night — Knight

1. The stars shone in the ____________________ sky.
2. In the north, ____________________ is longer in December than in June.
3. I've always wanted to see a ____________________ in shining armor.
4. The campers had to walk five miles at ____________________.
5. In the Middle Ages, a ____________________ wore so much armor he could barely walk.
6. She is working day and ____________________ to finish her project.
7. The ____________________ was dark and moonless.
8. One ____________________ had a golden sword.
9. It can't be ____________________ already!
10. A pale moon lit the ____________________ sky.
11. Most people sleep at ____________________.
12. That ____________________ is said to have fought dragons!
13. King Arthur's favorite ____________________ was seated on his right.
14. It is dangerous to be alone in the city at ____________________.
15. A wolf howled in the arctic ____________________.
16. Both a ____________________ and his horse wore armor.
17. The cat was as black as ____________________.
18. A white ____________________ is coming to the rescue.
19. She was surprised to learn that the _________________ was really a king.
20. We left a ____________________ light turned on in every room.

Name____

Date____

No — Know

1. Did you ____________________ it's your turn to do the dishes?
2. There is ____________________ way I could have done it.
3. ____________________, you may not have that last piece of pie.
4. I ____________________ I must have met you before now.
5. ____________________, I don't want to see you.
6. That girl doesn't ____________________ anyone here.
7. There were ____________________ people in the street.
8. I don't ____________________ what this word means.
9. Just tell me yes or ____________________.
10. She didn't ____________________ the answer.
11. The man said ____________________ to the beggar.
12. I'm scared because I don't ____________________ who's in the house.
13. I'm almost sure she will say ____________________.
14. She doesn't ____________________ my telephone number.
15. I'm not sure I ____________________ what will be on the test.
16. It's a fact that ____________________ one is sure that UFOs are from outer space.
17. I don't ____________________ who's calling, but it's for you.
18. There are ____________________ polar bears in the desert.
19. Didn't you ____________________ what would happen if you did that?
20. I'm sorry I have to say ____________________, but I can't come.

Name____

Date____

None — Nun

1. All her life she had wanted to be a ____________________.
2. It was surprising that ____________________ of them wanted ice cream.
3. I wonder why ____________________ of the fish will bite.
4. At 3:00, I was told that ____________________ of the racers had finished.
5. A ____________________ often wears a black and white outfit.
6. It seems that ____________________ of the assistants can help us.
7. My aunt is a ____________________ in Mexico.
8. It's frustrating that ____________________ of these ideas will really solve the problem.
9. Mother Teresa is probably the most famous ____________________.
10. I'm sorry, but ____________________ of the cookies are left.
11. In our school, ____________________ of the classes are crowded.
12. Her favorite teacher was a ____________________.
13. Should we talk to the priest or to a ____________________?
14. It's amazing that ____________________ of these socks match!
15. I'm afraid that ____________________ of your pictures came out.
16. Why is it that ____________________ of the checks arrived yesterday?
17. It takes faith and commitment to be a ____________________.
18. I hope that ____________________ of the messages will contain bad news!
19. It seems that ____________________ of the trails will take us there.
20. When she became a ____________________, she took on a new name.

Name____

Date____

Nose — Knows

1. I think my grandmother ____________________ everyone in town.
2. The teacher ____________________ who will win.
3. Her ____________________ was badly sunburned yesterday.
4. My ____________________ was broken in the accident.
5. Who ____________________ the answer to the first question?
6. A dog's ____________________ is supposed to be cool and moist.
7. Her ____________________ is bleeding.
8. No one ____________________ what happened.
9. Follow Mark. He ____________________ the way.
10. The horse always ____________________ when he's nearly home.
11. I had to blow my ____________________ a lot when I had that bad cold.
12. Pinocchio's ____________________ grew when he told a lie.
13. Some people think the owl ____________________ a lot because his big unblinking eyes make him look wise.
14. A pig's ____________________ is called a snout.
15. I'm sure someone ____________________ where the show will be.
16. It is better to breathe through your __________________ than your mouth.
17. She ____________________ I'm doing everything I can to help.
18. Sally ____________________ Spanish and French.
19. The dog's ____________________ twitched as he sniffed the air.
20. The ____________________ is the organ of smell.

Name____

Date____

Not — Knot

1. He said to tell you he's ____________________ coming today.
2. Jim's shoelaces were tied in a ____________________.
3. They have ____________________ written for several weeks.
4. You do ____________________ have to eat if you feel ill.
5. Use a square ____________________ to tie the two ropes together.
6. Do ____________________ enter. This is private property.
7. A sailor must learn to tie almost every kind of ____________________.
8. The mountain climber felt a ____________________ beginning to slip.
9. California did ____________________ have much rain last year.
10. She wrapped a scarf around her neck and tied a ____________________.
11. I'm sorry, we do ____________________ have enough money for that.
12. The doctor says you should ____________________ eat so much sugar.
13. The man used a strong ____________________ to tie up the boat.
14. Animals can ____________________ talk.
15. The kitten played with the yarn until it was one huge ________________.
16. The boy was tying a ____________________ in his shoelaces.
17. The fisherman tied one ____________________ after another as he mended his net.
18. Dogs do ____________________ usually eat vegetables.
19. My mother does ____________________ like to drink coffee.
20. The ____________________ in the tow rope is coming loose!

Name____

Date____

Off — Of

1. Take ____________________ your hat when you go inside.
2. Her birthday is the fifth ____________________ May.
3. She died ____________________ a heart attack.
4. Be sure all the lights are turned __________________ before you leave.
5. The store is about a mile ___________________ Highway 7 on Post Road.
6. The dress is made ____________________ cotton.
7. Mary took a bag ____________________ candy to the party.
8. I'm sure this is one ____________________ her favorite coats.
9. The lamp fell ____________________ the table.
10. One ____________________ us will be the leader.
11. It was on the table, but it must have fallen ____________________.
12. The fourth ____________________ July is Independence Day.
13. Cross these three things ____________________ your list.
14. The boy was afraid he would fall ____________________ the horse.
15. Why are so many ____________________ the people here in costume?
16. I jumped ____________________ the roof into a big soft haystack.
17. Turn the motor ____________________, please.
18. I like my job most ____________________ the time.
19. She dusted ____________________ the old desk.
20. Would you lend me a sheet ____________________ paper?

Name____

Date____

Oh — Owe

1. You ____________________ me a dollar.
2. ____________________ sir, can you help us?
3. ____________________ no!
4. I don't know how much I ____________________.
5. Don't worry. You don't ____________________ me anything.
6. "____________________!" she said in surprise.
7. How much do I ____________________ now?
8. ____________________ boy! Here we go again.
9. ____________________ please, may I have some?
10. ____________________ thank you! You have been so helpful!
11. ____________________, I don't really mind.
12. Please pay back what you ____________________ right away.
13. You ____________________ a lot of money, don't you?
14. We ____________________ them a dinner.
15. ____________________, isn't that beautiful?
16. Could you please find out how much I ____________________?
17. ____________________, I didn't really mean that!
18. Next month they'll pay back everything they ____________________.
19. You ____________________ him an apology, at least.
20. ____________________ waiter! Can you bring us some coffee?

Name____

Date____

One — Won

1. Do you know who ____________________ the race yesterday?
2. Jane ____________________ a trip to Hawaii!
3. I'm not sure which ____________________ is Mr. Jacobs.
4. It's easy to multiply and divide by ____________________.
5. I don't think this is the ____________________ you want.
6. The Green Bay Packers ____________________ the first Super Bowl.
7. Our team has ____________________ five out of seven games so far.
8. Is this the right ____________________?
9. We couldn't have ____________________ the game without your help.
10. My sister is the ____________________ in the pink blouse.
11. The first ____________________ is usually the best.
12. The only ____________________ here right now is Mr. Jones.
13. James ____________________ the spelling bee last year.
14. That's ____________________ of my favorite books.
15. At least we ____________________ a trophy for good sportsmanship.
16. She was my ____________________ and only helper.
17. I heard that ____________________ of the best fishing spots is near here.
18. The Battle of New Orleans took place after the Civil War had already been ____________________.
19. Sally would probably have ____________________, but she fell down.
20. I think he's ____________________ several awards.

Name____

Date____

Pail — Pale

1. Jack and Jill went up the hill to fetch a __________________ of water.
2. Most people look __________________ when they first get to Hawaii.
3. He dropped the __________________ into the well.
4. We used a __________________ to carry corn to the animals.
5. The boy looked quite __________________.
6. The __________________ was made of coated steel.
7. The dogs began to snarl and the lady turned __________________.
8. Each child took a __________________ out to pick berries.
9. She had blond hair and __________________ skin.
10. The dress was a __________________ pink.
11. A __________________ moon lit their way.
12. The __________________ was soon filled with warm milk.
13. The man was riding a __________________ horse.
14. When my mother heard the news, she turned __________________.
15. Don’t use this __________________ for water. It has a hole in it.
16. The little __________________ was full of pennies she’d collected.
17. This __________________ needs to be washed.
18. The mountains looked __________________ in the moonlight.
19. Let me see if I can find another __________________ for you.
20. You look wonderful in __________________ colors.

Name____

Date____

Pain — Pane

1. There was a sharp ____________________ in her elbow.
2. Take two aspirin to relieve the ____________________.
3. One ____________________ of glass was missing.
4. The old dog was in a lot of ____________________.
5. The baseball shattered a large ____________________ of glass.
6. Sometimes my little brother is a ____________________.
7. He'd never been in so much ____________________!
8. The window ____________________ was beginning to crack.
9. The ____________________ in my shoulder is getting worse.
10. A ____________________ had to be cut especially for this window.
11. Crying can heal the ____________________ in your heart.
12. He was very thankful that he felt no ____________________.
13. Doctor, I can hardly stand the ____________________!
14. Every ____________________ of the stained glass window was a different color.
15. I need to replace a ____________________ of glass in my car.
16. A wild animal in ____________________ can be very dangerous.
17. We're going to paint a sign on the largest window ________________.
18. He must be in ____________________, but he hasn't said anything.
19. The ____________________ in my feet makes it hard to walk.
20. A burn can cause more ____________________ than many injuries.

Name____

Date____

Pair — Pare — Pear

1. Would you like a ____________________ or a peach?
2. This ____________________ of shoes is almost new.
3. I only have one ____________________ of socks without holes.
4. She used a small knife to ____________________ the vegetables.
5. You must ____________________ up with someone else for this game.
6. This ____________________ tastes wonderful!
7. I'm trying to find a clean ____________________ of pants.
8. There are a ____________________ of climbers on the mountain.
9. Please ____________________ these potatoes for me.
10. I like to put cottage cheese on a canned ____________________.
11. I got a ____________________ of sunglasses for only $2.00 yesterday.
12. Mark lent his little sister a ____________________ of gloves.
13. What an interesting ____________________ they are!
14. This ____________________ isn't ripe enough to eat quite yet.
15. Mother put a ____________________ in my lunch.
16. We bought a ____________________ of tickets for the play.
17. Don't ____________________ too much off of those vegetables.
18. My grandfather has a ____________________ tree in his yard.
19. May I borrow a ____________________ of scissors?
20. I think this is ____________________ juice.

Name____

Date____

Passed — Past

1. I was excited to learn that I ____________________ the science test.
2. The story takes place in the ____________________.
3. The car drove ____________________ the house slowly.
4. The ____________________ is over and we can't change it.
5. The quarterback ____________________ the football.
6. History is a study of the ____________________.
7. The old man ____________________ us on his way to the store.
8. We ____________________ a police car.
9. A herd of horses galloped ____________________ the house.
10. I think we ____________________ the turnoff a few minutes ago.
11. That was the ____________________ and this is the present.
12. An hour ____________________ before anyone came.
13. I can't believe the bus drove right ____________________ me.
14. As they ____________________ her house, the dog ran out barking.
15. There have been many wars in the ____________________.
16. He said not to dwell on the ____________________.
17. They slowed down as they ____________________ the store.
18. Mother ____________________ the butter to Sam.
19. Everyone ____________________ the test.
20. Many young people were walking ____________________ the store.

Name____

Date____

Patience — Patients

1. Three __________________ were still in the waiting room.
2. I don't have too much __________________ with him anymore.
3. The report said that more __________________ were admitted to the hospital in 2006 than in any other year.
4. The emergency room was ready for __________________.
5. Eagles have incredible __________________. They can sit for hours.
6. The nurse visits her __________________ at least five times a day.
7. Americans are not known for their __________________.
8. Waiting four months for her leg to heal tested her ________________.
9. I began visiting with one of the other __________________.
10. It takes __________________ and hard work to reach goals.
11. We visited the hospital to sing carols to the __________________.
12. Doctors who have too many __________________ can get very tired.
13. Our dog has a lot of __________________ most of the time.
14. The man didn't have much __________________ with children.
15. The diet of these __________________ must be carefully controlled.
16. The Chinese are noted for their __________________.
17. The ________________ were unhappy with their medicine.
18. It is hard to wait in a long line unless you have __________________.
19. The doctor visited all of his hospital __________________ every day.
20. It takes __________________ to make a quilt.

Name____

Date____

Pause — Paws

1. We are going to ____________________ for station identification.
2. I saw the bird ____________________ before it flitted away.
3. Spot’s ____________________ are all muddy.
4. Don’t be silly! Horses don’t have ____________________!
5. When reading, it’s a good idea to ____________________ every fifteen minutes or so and look away from the book.
6. My dog loves to have his ____________________ rubbed.
7. After a long ____________________, the man began to speak.
8. We will ____________________ here for a few minutes to rest.
9. Bear ____________________ can be over 12 inches long!
10. The tracks showed wolf ____________________ of three different sizes.
11. The old lady would often ____________________ to remember old times.
12. There was a short ____________________ before the speaker began.
13. It’s hard to get anything done if you ____________________ too often.
14. My dog has hair growing from his ____________________.
15. I had to ____________________ again to read the directions.
16. His ____________________ must hurt. He can hardly walk.
17. People have feet and hands rather than ____________________.
18. I have to ____________________ for a moment to think about this.
19. Animals with ____________________ are generally good at digging.
20. The puppy doesn’t like it when I tickle his ____________________.

Name____

Date____

Peace — Piece

1. Please pass me a ____________________ of pie.
2. The puzzle was missing just one ____________________.
3. You will need a new ____________________ of paper.
4. Many people pray for world ____________________.
5. Christmas is a season of ____________________ for many.
6. You can disagree with others and still be at ____________________ with them.
7. Would you like a ____________________ of candy?
8. He cut himself on a ____________________ of broken glass.
9. Every neighborhood likes ____________________ and quiet.
10. Did you ever find the missing ____________________?
11. The Indian chiefs passed the ____________________ pipe.
12. The father wanted to be at ____________________ with his son.
13. I'll have a ____________________ of bread, please.
14. The dove is a symbol of ____________________.
15. The two nations signed a ____________________ treaty.
16. We'll need another ____________________ of wood to start the fire.
17. Fireworks shattered the ____________________ of the evening.
18. This ____________________ of cloth would make a nice shirt.
19. I got the first ____________________ of birthday cake.
20. R.I.P. means "rest in ____________________."

Name____

Date____

Peak — Peek

1. We saw a little girl __________________ into the room.
2. They began climbing to the highest __________________.
3. He was tempted to __________________ through the keyhole.
4. The __________________ could barely be seen through the clouds.
5. Let's __________________ through the window to see if anyone's here.
6. The sun set behind a __________________.
7. Most athletes reach their __________________ performance when they are young.
8. The boy stood on his tiptoes to __________________ into the store.
9. Don't __________________ when you're playing hide and seek.
10. The pilot flew low over the __________________.
11. The __________________ of his success came when he was 40 years old.
12. The climbers reached the __________________ at 10:00 in the morning.
13. Don't __________________! It's a secret.
14. Mother said the cake will fall if we __________________ into the oven.
15. A strong wind was blowing snow off the __________________.
16. She took a dog sled to the __________________ of that mountain!
17. The sun might __________________ through the clouds this afternoon.
18. Mt. Everest has the highest __________________ in the world.
19. The cat moved forward to __________________ out from under the bed.
20. A large bird landed near the __________________.

Name____

Date____

Peal — Peel

1. The bells began to ____________________.
2. Would you please ____________________ this carrot for me?
3. The sunburn caused her skin to ____________________.
4. I heard a ____________________ of laughter.
5. I began to ____________________ off my wet clothes.
6. Don't throw that orange ____________________ out the window!
7. She started to ____________________ the hard-boiled egg.
8. The ____________________ of church bells echoed through the valley.
9. Monkeys look cute when they ____________________ bananas.
10. You can ____________________ an onion again and again until there is nothing left.
11. A tomato is difficult to ____________________.
12. A ____________________ of laughter drifted across the meadow.
13. Mickey Mouse slipped on a banana ____________________.
14. People hurried to church as the bells began to ____________________.
15. The crash caused metal on the car to ____________________ back.
16. Most of the vitamins in a vegetable are in its ____________________.
17. The soldier had a hundred potatoes to ____________________.
18. The organ notes sounded like a ____________________ of bells.
19. The boys started to ____________________ the wrappers off the candy.
20. It was harder than she thought to ____________________ the stickers off.

Name____

Date____

Plain — Plane

1. The jewels were in ____________________ sight!
2. Our ____________________ leaves at midnight tonight.
3. My first trip on a ____________________ was scary.
4. The police officer wore ____________________ clothing.
5. It was a ____________________ cake with no frosting.
6. She was just ____________________ tired.
7. The ____________________ flew low over the river.
8. I like my ice cream ____________________.
9. Our ____________________ had to circle for an hour waiting to land.
10. I just want a ____________________ jacket—nothing special.
11. We traveled by ____________________ and bus on our vacation.
12. We bought a small ____________________ last year.
13. The girl was dressed in a ____________________ blue shirt and jeans.
14. The ____________________ nearly crashed in the ocean.
15. The material she chose for her dress was very ____________________.
16. The bird looked almost like a ____________________ flying in the sky.
17. Our ____________________ was a DC-10.
18. Clark Kent is a ____________________ person compared to Superman.
19. The meaning is ____________________ to see.
20. Many animals were grazing on the ____________________.

Name____

Date____

Principal — Principle

1. Our school has a great ____________________.
2. The ____________________ is my pal.
3. The ____________________ of the loan is $250.00.
4. Our ____________________ purpose for calling is to ask how we can help.
5. Our lawyer is a man of ____________________.
6. The first ____________________ is not to drive when you drink.
7. Gravity is a ____________________ of nature.
8. Our ____________________ likes to ice skate with the kids.
9. Telling the truth is a moral ____________________.
10. They were paying more interest than ____________________ on the loan.
11. What bothers me is the ____________________ of the matter. It doesn't seem right to me.
12. The mayor thinks the ____________________ of honesty is especially important.
13. The ____________________ reason they moved was to be near the family.
14. Martin had to see the ____________________ when he got in trouble.
15. I had to pay $10.00 ____________________ a week plus interest.
16. The ____________________ told everyone the rules of the school.
17. The ____________________ of equal rights is important in the U.S.
18. He voted against the idea on ____________________.
19. The ____________________ use of our old truck is to haul firewood.
20. They each had to pay half of the ____________________ on the loan.

Name____
Date____

Profit — Prophet

1. The company is finally making a good ____________________.
2. A ____________________ can tell the future.
3. The ____________________ on each item in a grocery store is low.
4. Elijah was a ____________________ in the Bible.
5. A company's ____________________ is money left after expenses.
6. Most oil companies make a very large ____________________.
7. He must think he's a ____________________ or something.
8. People would probably listen to a true ____________________.
9. The restaurant is just beginning to make a ____________________.
10. They wished they could ask a ____________________ about the future.
11. They didn't make a ____________________ last year. They had a loss.
12. A company which can't make a ____________________ will fail.
13. Which person here is pretending to be a ____________________?
14. The ____________________ said it would not rain for many years.
15. The king wanted to kill the ____________________.
16. Believe me! She is no ____________________.
17. This year's ____________________ was the biggest ever for our store.
18. Almost everyone can ____________________ from instruction.
19. No one believed the man was really a ____________________.
20. If they cut expenses, they can increase their ____________________.

Name____

Date____

Quite — Quiet

1. The room was ____________________ as the crowd waited.
2. The old lady was ____________________ friendly.
3. We weren't ____________________ sure what time it was.
4. The forest was beautiful and ____________________.
5. It wasn't ____________________ 5:00 when the guests began to arrive.
6. The children were hardly ever ____________________ for long.
7. "I'm not ____________________ ready," said Jane.
8. The neighbors complain if our dogs are not ____________________.
9. Butterflies are ____________________ when they fly.
10. We're not ____________________ ready for the party.
11. The sea was ____________________ as they sailed along.
12. The picture on the wall was ____________________ beautiful.
13. The California Redwood is ____________________ tall.
14. If you are very ____________________, you might see a wild animal.
15. Many people like their homes to be ____________________ and private.
16. No one was ____________________ ready to go yet.
17. Mornings are a good time to walk because it's so ____________________.
18. Honey is ____________________ good on toast.
19. I'm ____________________ sure he was at the restaurant last night.
20. Please be ____________________ so everyone can hear.

Name____

Date____

Rain — Rein — Reign

1. The man was making a new __________________ for his horse.
2. They wanted a king to __________________ the country.
3. She dropped a __________________ and the horse stumbled.
4. The summer __________________ washed the leaves.
5. It was cloudy and looked like it might __________________.
6. Kings and queens __________________ in foreign countries.
7. The __________________ was falling hard.
8. The horse stood still whenever his __________________ was dropped.
9. Some people like __________________ better than sunshine.
10. The greedy king wanted to __________________ over a large area.
11. In the Sahara Desert, plants sprout quickly after a __________________.
12. King Henry's __________________ was important in English history.
13. Everything seems fresh and green after a __________________.
14. She pulled on the __________________ to turn her horse to the left.
15. The __________________ broke and he lost control of his mount.
16. They hoped it wouldn't __________________ the day of the picnic.
17. Queen Margaret began to __________________ when her husband died.
18. Seventy-four inches of __________________ once fell in a single day!
19. The bridle is fine but one __________________ needs to be replaced.
20. Americans do not want a king to __________________ over them.

Name____

Date____

Raise — Rays

1. Beautiful ____________________ of sunlight shone through the clouds.
2. We need to ____________________ money for our club.
3. It takes the __________________ of the sun eight minutes to reach the earth.
4. There are a few ____________________ of hope.
5. It's time to ____________________ the flag.
6. The powerful ____________________ of a spotlight searched the area.
7. The first ____________________ of sunlight peeked over the mountains.
8. He has decided to ____________________ chickens.
9. We plan to ____________________ goats on the farm.
10. The store will ____________________ the price on these soon.
11. The ____________________ of their flashlights were getting weak.
12. She has always wanted to ____________________ her own vegetables.
13. The last ____________________ of sunlight were fading from the sky.
14. We can ____________________ the sails now.
15. I saw a deer ____________________ its head and look around.
16. Silvery ____________________ of moonlight sparkled on the snow.
17. Laser ____________________ are very powerful.
18. Be sure to ____________________ your hand if you wish to speak.
19. The aliens used death ____________________ to defend themselves.
20. He began to ____________________ the garage door.

Name____

Date____

Rap — Wrap

1. Suddenly there was a ____________________ on the door.
2. I am almost ready to ____________________ the gifts.
3. Please don't ____________________ your fingers on the desk.
4. Please ____________________ the fish in newspaper.
5. It's cold, so we'd better ____________________ up.
6. Plastic is used to ____________________ food to keep it fresh.
7. A woodpecker began to ____________________ on the tree.
8. I thought I heard a ____________________ on the window.
9. We'll ____________________ the wet swimsuits in some towels.
10. He used to ____________________ his fingers when he was thinking.
11. I had waited at the table for so long that I began to ____________________ my fingers impatiently.
12. I'd better ____________________ the box so I can get it in the mail.
13. We stopped in terror when we heard a ____________________ echoing from deep within the old mine.
14. Just ____________________ on the window if you want in.
15. Be sure to ____________________ things carefully so they don't break.
16. He tried to ____________________ the gift back up exactly the same way.
17. Don't ____________________ that box yet. It's not quite ready.
18. It bothers me when you ____________________ on the side of your glass.
19. We watched the butcher carefully ____________________ the chicken.
20. It's important to ____________________ bread so it doesn't dry out.

Name____

Date____

Read — Red

1. Pam ____________________ a very good book.
2. Have you ____________________ my letter yet?
3. His hat is ____________________.
4. The teacher ____________________ us a poem.
5. The flag is ____________________, white and blue.
6. They ____________________ the story together.
7. The tablecloth is bright ____________________.
8. Stop when the light is ____________________.
9. That girl's ____________________ hair is pretty.
10. We are going to paint the walls ____________________.
11. Sam hasn't ____________________ the directions yet.
12. I thought fire engines were supposed to be ____________________.
13. He will be wearing a ____________________ shirt.
14. Haven't you ____________________ the signs?
15. Dad drove the car and Mom ____________________ the map.
16. The barn is ____________________ and brown.
17. Sally ____________________ everything she could about birds.
18. Mr. Smith ____________________ the school rules aloud.
19. Tom ____________________ the note to himself.
20. A ____________________ warning light was flashing.

Name____

Date____

Reads — Reeds

1. Our teacher ____________________ to us every day.
2. The ____________________ were bending in the breeze.
3. My dad ____________________ the newspaper every morning.
4. A great blue heron was standing in the ____________________.
5. She ____________________, but I'm not sure she understands.
6. Usually, ____________________ grow where there is a lot of water.
7. My sister ____________________ faster than anyone in her class.
8. Whoever ____________________ the most books will win a prize.
9. An animal was moving slowly through the ____________________.
10. We saw the ____________________ and were glad we had rubber boots.
11. Jack ____________________ sports magazines, but not many books.
12. We headed toward the ____________________ at the edge of the lake.
13. No one ____________________ more than my brother.
14. I think he ____________________ too many comic books!
15. A blind person ____________________ with his fingers.
16. The canoe slipped quietly through the tall ____________________.
17. Some ____________________ can grow 20 feet high.
18. He never ____________________ the directions.
19. A big moose was grazing in the ____________________.
20. It looked more like grass than ____________________.

Name____

Date____

Real — Reel

1. The mountains were so beautiful they didn't look __________________.
2. The halibut ____________________ held miles of line.
3. My fishing ____________________ is tangled up again.
4. I wonder if he's the ____________________ thief.
5. Most of what is on TV is not ____________________.
6. He began to ____________________ in the fighting trout.
7. He was so tired he began seeing things that weren't __________________.
8. My pole is fine, but I need a new ____________________.
9. It was the first ____________________ castle he'd ever seen.
10. We're in ____________________ trouble now.
11. Don't ____________________ in your line too fast.
12. I lost the fish because my ____________________ fell off.
13. I can't tell you too much about his ____________________ job.
14. His new ____________________ cost at least $450.
15. I'd sure like to know the ____________________ reason for this.
16. Fly fishermen use a special kind of ____________________.
17. This book is supposed to tell the ____________________ story.
18. The fish was so big I almost couldn't ____________________ it in.
19. This is the best rod and ____________________ I've ever owned!
20. I don't think we've heard the ____________________ truth yet.

Name____

Date____

Right — Write

1. You're ____________________ about that!
2. Please ____________________ when you get there.
3. I can't tell if this is ____________________ or wrong.
4. Do you know if he's ____________________?
5. He can ____________________ really well.
6. Nothing looks quite ____________________ in this room.
7. I am going to ____________________ a letter to my grandparents.
8. We have to ____________________ a poem about Thanksgiving.
9. Turn ____________________ at the next corner.
10. Please ____________________ what you want me to buy for you on a list.
11. Raise your ____________________ hand.
12. His house is on the ____________________ side of the street.
13. People who can't ____________________ neatly can learn to type.
14. He always thinks he's ____________________ and everyone else is wrong.
15. It's important to wear the ____________________ clothes if it's cold out.
16. It is necessary to learn to ____________________ if you want a good job.
17. I hope you are doing the ____________________ thing.
18. It can be interesting to ____________________ in a journal and read it a year or two later.
19. My uncle used to ____________________ books for children.
20. It's against the rules to ____________________ notes in class.

Name____

Date____

Ring — Wring

1. My mother's ____________________ is very old.
2. The church bells began to ____________________.
3. We'd better ____________________ out these wet clothes.
4. There is a ____________________ around the tub that we should clean.
5. The lady was so upset she began to ____________________ her hands.
6. It is easier to ____________________ wet jeans when two people work together.
7. Sometimes you can see a ____________________ around the moon.
8. Please ____________________ out those socks.
9. That teacup should be washed again. I see a ____________________ in it.
10. The telephone began to ____________________.
11. Hurry and get to your seat! The bell will ____________________ soon.
12. Don't forget to ____________________ out the washcloth and hang it up.
13. Stop talking when I ____________________ the bell.
14. I tried to ____________________ as much water from my hair as I could.
15. I think I heard the doorbell ____________________.
16. I'm afraid my ears are bad. They ____________________ all the time.
17. The trail made a ____________________ around the lake.
18. Please take these towels outside and ____________________ them out.
19. Be careful when you ____________________ out that sweater.
20. I love to hear the bells ____________________ across the valley.

Name____

Date____

Road — Rode

1. Jack ____________________ his motorcycle to Florida.
2. Which ____________________ are we supposed to take?
3. The dog ____________________ in the back seat.
4. It's not a very good ____________________.
5. There's no ____________________ to the cabin.
6. They ____________________ the Ferris wheel several times.
7. A sign said that the ____________________ was closed.
8. Our ____________________ is not yet plowed.
9. Check the map! I don't know if we're on the right ____________________.
10. We ____________________ in the back of the truck.
11. Who ____________________ my bicycle yesterday?
12. If you travel down this ____________________ for 20 miles, you will be in Mexico.
13. The clowns each ____________________ a unicycle.
14. What a bumpy ____________________ this is!
15. Only one ____________________ leads south from here.
16. The cowboy ____________________ his favorite horse to town.
17. We need a good ____________________ map.
18. Three people ____________________ in the boat.
19. We all ____________________ the train into the park.
20. The musher ____________________ in the dogsled whenever he could.

Name____

Date____

Sail — Sale

1. I've always wanted to __________________ around the world.
2. Once he was out on the water, he raised the first __________________.
3. This shirt was on __________________ at the mall.
4. They finally saw a __________________ out on the ocean.
5. The __________________ of cigarettes to children is illegal.
6. Everything in the store is on __________________.
7. Since he was three, he'd dreamed of learning to __________________.
8. We have a garage __________________ every spring.
9. My old car is for __________________.
10. When I am discouraged, I like to imagine that I'll __________________ away someday to see the world.
11. This __________________ is torn and needs to be repaired.
12. Don't spend all of your money at the __________________.
13. Is this house for __________________?
14. It is easier to __________________ with the wind than against it.
15. We passed a sign that said, "Puppies for __________________."
16. My friends built a boat and plan to __________________ for a year.
17. I could see a tiny __________________ far out on the lake.
18. Save money now at the __________________ of the century!
19. I'm sorry, but this horse is not for __________________.
20. Many people in Chicago like to __________________ on the lake.

Name____

Date____

Scene — Seen

1. What a beautiful ____________________!
2. I haven't ____________________ that movie yet.
3. Have you ____________________ your sister lately?
4. The police just arrived at the ____________________ of the accident.
5. No one has ____________________ anything strange lately.
6. The sunset ____________________ made a great photograph.
7. This must be the strangest ____________________ ever!
8. I wish I could have ____________________ you when you were in town.
9. Has anyone ____________________ my purse?
10. They've ____________________ a bear in the neighborhood.
11. A detective visited the ____________________ of the crime.
12. The children had ____________________ a dog on the playground.
13. It was an unexpected ____________________.
14. They'd never ____________________ the northern lights before.
15. An atom is so small it cannot be ____________________.
16. The castle on the hilltop made a nice ____________________.
17. It was a peaceful ____________________.
18. The ____________________ was changing quickly.
19. He wishes he'd ____________________ the news last night.
20. The ____________________ from this window is the best.

Name____

Date____

Sea — See

1. I hope we'll __________________ a whale!
2. Did you __________________ the show yet?
3. The __________________ sparkled in the sunlight.
4. We will probably __________________ you tomorrow.
5. What did you __________________ there?
6. The sun was rising over the __________________.
7. Many ships were lost at __________________ that summer.
8. The __________________ looked dark and dangerous.
9. Water from the __________________ is too salty to drink.
10. We're going to __________________ a movie tonight.
11. I __________________ something moving on the hillside.
12. The Mediterranean is a large __________________.
13. Did anyone here __________________ the eclipse?
14. I think I __________________ what you mean now.
15. My eyes don't __________________ as well as they once did.
16. Millions of salmon return from the __________________ each year.
17. Can you __________________ the tiny insects in the grass?
18. Hundreds of birds were soaring above the __________________.
19. A soft wind from the __________________ rippled the grass.
20. People once used the stars to find their way across the

    __________________.

Name____

Date____

Seam — Seem

1. There doesn't ____________________ to be any problem.
2. They ____________________ to be looking for something.
3. The ____________________ of my shirt is coming apart.
4. You don't ____________________ to be afraid at all!
5. The teacher showed us how to sew a ____________________.
6. These books ____________________ to be the best.
7. This shouldn't tear. It has a double ____________________.
8. It didn't ____________________ warm because of the wind.
9. You ____________________ very tired today.
10. That ____________________ is crooked.
11. He doesn't ____________________ to understand what happened.
12. This just doesn't ____________________ right to me.
13. Those houses ____________________ to be empty.
14. The cookies ____________________ to be done.
15. The ____________________ ripped when I reached up too far.
16. My rubber boot is leaking at the ____________________.
17. Those people don't ____________________ to know we're watching them.
18. I should seal every ____________________ in this raincoat. It leaks!
19. Those people ____________________ to be in a very big hurry.
20. The coat was so well made that you couldn't see a ____________________.

Name____

Date____

Sense — Since

1. Common ____________________ is important.
2. We have lived here ____________________ 1999.
3. He doesn't have much ____________________ when it comes to money.
4. The alarm has been set ____________________ 5:00 last night.
5. Things have been better ____________________ you came.
6. It has been sunny ____________________ Tuesday.
7. Cows don't have a lot of ____________________.
8. I've wanted to meet you ____________________ I first heard about you.
9. It just makes ____________________ to wait and see.
10. People don't depend too much on their ____________________ of smell.
11. She's been cooking ____________________ 9:00 this morning.
12. Our yard light can ____________________ motion.
13. I haven't heard from Mrs. Smith ____________________ June.
14. He's been reading books ____________________ he was three years old.
15. Things have gotten worse ____________________ the year began.
16. I could ____________________ that something was wrong.
17. In the dark, your ____________________ of hearing is important.
18. People have lived in this town ____________________ 1802.
19. It doesn't make ____________________ to avoid doing homework.
20. The dog could ____________________ that someone was coming.

Name____

Date____

Sew — So — Sow

1. It has been ____________________ long since I've seen you!
2. She's learning to ____________________ her own clothes.
3. Farmers ____________________ in the spring and reap in the fall.
4. It's too bad you live ____________________ far away.
5. I've never been ____________________ surprised in all my life!
6. Mary is going to ____________________ some curtains for the lodge.
7. The Farmer's Almanac tells when it's best to __________________ crops.
8. A gardener can't reap what she doesn't ____________________.
9. I've never seen ____________________ many people in one place!
10. Their mother likes to _______________, but she doesn't enjoy mending.
11. The instructions say to ____________________ the seeds in moist soil.
12. I'm ____________________ happy! I don't know what to say!
13. She bought some beautiful fabric to ____________________ into a skirt.
14. It takes a special machine to ____________________ upholstery.
15. I can't believe this costs ____________________ much!
16. The sunset is ____________________ beautiful tonight!
17. When do you plan to ____________________ your garden?
18. This seam is ripped. I'd better ____________________ it up.
19. A tailorbird uses its bill to ____________________ a large leaf into a nest.
20. If you ____________________ smiles, you will reap happiness.

Name____

Date____

Soar — Sore

1. We saw a hawk ____________________ through the sky.
2. His thumb is ____________________ because he hit it with a hammer.
3. How's your ____________________ foot?
4. With his hang glider, he can really ____________________!
5. When I fly a kite, I imagine that I can ____________________ away with it.
6. Janet stayed home from school with a ____________________ throat.
7. The new skyscraper will ____________________ above the city.
8. How does an eagle ____________________ without flapping its wings?
9. My muscles are so ____________________ today I can hardly move.
10. She's been reading for so long that her eyes are ____________________.
11. Our dog has a ____________________ in his ear.
12. A glider can ____________________ for many miles.
13. Please don't touch my sunburn. It's still ____________________.
14. I wonder if we can get this paper airplane to ____________________ through that second-story window.
15. The pilot loved to ____________________ high above the mountains.
16. We watched the balloons ____________________ upwards until they disappeared into the clouds.
17. I'm so glad my knee isn't ____________________ anymore.
18. A gust of wind caused the feather to ____________________.
19. My toe is really ____________________! I must have broken it.
20. The boy had a painful ____________________ on his right leg.

Name____

Date____

Some — Sum

1. The ____________________ of five and seven is twelve.
2. I think that ____________________ of the books have gotten wet.
3. May I have ____________________ butter, please?
4. Let me ____________________ up what I think you're saying.
5. This will take ____________________ time, so please be patient.
6. Just a moment and I'll figure out the ____________________.
7. I'd be surprised if there weren't ____________________ letters for you.
8. I've read that ____________________ of the animals in the zoo are ill.
9. She had completed all but one ____________________ correctly.
10. We'd better try to find ____________________ water to drown the fire.
11. Who knows the ____________________ of eight and nine?
12. There are ____________________ children splashing in the stream.
13. We need to buy ____________________ food.
14. The lawyer is ready to ____________________ up her arguments.
15. I always check each ____________________ before turning in a test.
16. I think ____________________ squirrels are nesting near the house.
17. Could I have ____________________ cream in my coffee, please?
18. We're going to plant ____________________ trees today.
19. Would you check this ____________________ for me?
20. It looks as if ____________________ paint has dripped onto the carpet.

Name____

Date____

Son — Sun

1. This is my ____________________ Mark.
2. The ____________________ is finally shining!
3. Don't look straight at the ____________________. It can hurt your eyes.
4. John is their oldest ____________________.
5. He isn't her ____________________. He's her nephew.
6. These plants need a lot of ____________________.
7. Janet's ____________________ is a doctor.
8. It's a hundred degrees today in the ____________________.
9. Too much ____________________ can cause bad burns.
10. The ____________________ is 96 million miles away.
11. The ____________________ of the president is a writer.
12. The ____________________ shines into this room every morning.
13. My teacher's ____________________ is nineteen.
14. Our ____________________ is one of many stars in the Milky Way galaxy.
15. The ____________________ will rise at 5:00 in the morning.
16. My ____________________ is a doctor.
17. That tall man is Martha's ____________________.
18. He doesn't want anyone to know his ____________________ is in prison.
19. She spends a lot of time with her youngest ____________________.
20. The ____________________ always sets in the west.

Name____

Date____

Stairs — Stares

1. Be careful not to fall down the __________________.
2. I hate it when my little sister __________________ at people.
3. The children had to climb 120 __________________ to the school.
4. These __________________ are dangerous and need repair.
5. Mark just __________________ at the ground sometimes.
6. He loves stars, so he __________________ into space a lot at night.
7. Be very careful. The __________________ squeak and you might awaken someone.
8. Do you know why he just sits and __________________ at the wall?
9. It will cost a lot more to carpet the __________________.
10. A set of circular __________________ led to the top of the tower.
11. Don't run up the __________________.
12. Old Mrs. Winston __________________ out to sea all day.
13. Inside the cave, dusty __________________ led down into the darkness.
14. An old owl sits on that post each night and __________________ around.
15. I don't like it when Janet __________________ at me!
16. Mary __________________ her friend in the eyes when she's mad.
17. Please sweep and scrub the __________________.
18. No one __________________ better than my cousin in a contest.
19. The men carved __________________ into the snow over the pass.
20. She __________________ whenever she's thinking hard.

Name____

Date____

Stationary — Stationery

1. The office has already run out of ____________________.
2. The jet looked as if it were ____________________ in the sky.
3. The ____________________ I got for my birthday was very pretty.
4. I would like to write, but I'm all out of ____________________.
5. The animal was perfectly ____________________ as we approached.
6. The equipment was ____________________.
7. The burglar was ____________________ until everything became quiet.
8. For my birthday, I got a ____________________ set with flowers on it.
9. My sister wants me to buy her some ____________________.
10. Most businesses have their own printed ____________________.
11. The turtle remained ____________________ until the fox wandered away.
12. The boy was ____________________ even after I asked him to move.
13. The ____________________ smelled like flowers.
14. We were ____________________ as the deer walked by.
15. She got a new ____________________ set for her desk.
16. The girl was ____________________ until someone shouted her name.
17. The machines were ____________________ in the fields.
18. I have a set of cartoon ____________________.
19. The soldiers on guard were perfectly ____________________.
20. The ____________________ was printed with gold ink.

Name____

Date____

Steak — Stake

1. I'm going to order __________________ and potatoes.
2. Would you rather have __________________ or roast?
3. We placed a __________________ on each corner of the land.
4. I'd like my __________________ well done, please.
5. The men were finally ready to __________________ their claim.
6. This ________________ shows that there are underground wires here.
7. I think we've lost a tent __________________.
8. The price of __________________ has really gone up lately.
9. No one really knows what is at __________________ here.
10. The __________________ is generally more tender if cattle are fattened.
11. Flank __________________ is often made into corned beef.
12. Chuck __________________ is not too expensive.
13. New York __________________ does not have any bones.
14. According to legend, a vampire can be killed by driving a __________________ through its heart.
15. He has little at __________________, so he doesn't really care.
16. The new lightweight tents use this aluminum __________________.
17. We love __________________ cooked over charcoal.
18. Hamburger is sometimes called Salisbury __________________.
19. They were careful to __________________ their gold claim correctly.
20. The police department was planning a __________________ out.

Name____

Date____

Steal — Steel

1. It is against the law to ____________________.
2. The boys promised never to ____________________.
3. These nails are made with ____________________.
4. Iron is not as strong as ____________________.
5. I need some ____________________ pipe.
6. No one would ____________________ that old rusty car!
7. The thieves tried to ____________________ her wallet.
8. Iron will rust, but stainless ____________________ will not.
9. The treasure was guarded so that no one could ____________________ it.
10. He tried to ____________________ my pencil!
11. All of the pots and pans were made of ____________________.
12. We were afraid someone might ____________________ our money.
13. There are so many locks and alarms that it would be impossible to ____________________ anything from there.
14. They met late at night to plan a way to ____________________ the gold.
15. Sunlight sparkled on the ____________________ of the factory.
16. One of the most useful metals known is ____________________.
17. The runner tried to ____________________ second base.
18. Shoplifting is one way to ____________________.
19. The knife was made of stainless ____________________.
20. Airplanes are made of aluminum, not ____________________.

Name____

Date____

Tacks — Tax

1. Nearly everyone who earns money pays income __________________.
2. Mary __________________ her grocery list on the bulletin board.
3. Property __________________ usually pays for schools and education.
4. It seems like I pay so much ________________ that I can’t save money.
5. A bucket of __________________ had spilled on the road.
6. The carpet was held down firmly with __________________.
7. I got a notice from the _________________ office that I had overpaid.
8. No one likes to pay __________________.
9. A few states have no sales __________________.
10. Round metal thumb __________________ can be dangerous because they fall with the point up.
11. We need more __________________ to finish this bulletin board.
12. I’m not sure how many _________________ we’ll need to hold this up.
13. Sales __________________ on a car can be hundreds of dollars.
14. Should I use nails or __________________ for this?
15. Everyone is angry about the new __________________ increase.
16. Those __________________ are rusty and should be thrown away.
17. The __________________ are coming loose.
18. The President said there would be no __________________ increases.
19. I can write this expense off as a __________________ deduction.
20. She said we should buy some more thumb __________________.

Name____

Date____

Tail — Tale

1. I don't think it's the truth. I'm sure it's just a ____________________.
2. Look! The dog's wagging his ____________________. He's friendly!
3. This is my favorite fairy ____________________.
4. The very tip of the cat's ____________________ was twitching.
5. Her horse's ____________________ hangs almost to the ground.
6. The ____________________ of a rat has no hair.
7. I love to read any ____________________ of the Old West.
8. The leader of a wolf pack carries his ____________________ high.
9. Paul Bunyan is the hero of this tall ____________________.
10. This story is a ____________________ of ancient Egypt.
11. Almost every folk ____________________ was passed down by word of mouth for years before it was written.
12. A kite needs a longer ____________________ when the wind is strong.
13. It's never a good idea to pull an animal's ____________________.
14. I'm not sure whether to believe that ____________________ or not!
15. She dressed up as a unicorn, but her ____________________ fell off.
16. This is a ____________________ about Peter Rabbit.
17. My dog's ____________________ is so short he can't wag it.
18. The storyteller told a funny little ____________________.
19. This is not just a ____________________! It's the truth!
20. Look at what a bushy ____________________ that squirrel has!

Name____

Date____

Then — Than

1. I am taller ____________________ my mom.
2. I think I was at home ____________________.
3. We went through a town, ____________________ over a hill.
4. Sam is a lot older ____________________ Jim.
5. We are bigger now ____________________ we used to be.
6. My bike is better ____________________ yours.
7. He called first, ____________________ he came over.
8. I can spell better ____________________ you.
9. Things were different back ____________________.
10. First the band played, ____________________ the fireworks began.
11. I'd rather play ____________________ go to the store.
12. Back ____________________ I had long hair.
13. Ten is more ____________________ two.
14. We'll do some work and ____________________ read a book.
15. This house is a lot nicer ____________________ the last one we had.
16. First we'll eat, ____________________ we'll go for a walk.
17. Real flowers are better ____________________ silk ones.
18. I think you know more ____________________ I do about cats.
19. It's a lot bigger ____________________ it used to be.
20. I'd rather go ____________________ because I'm busy now.

Name____

Date____

There — Their

1. I think ____________________ sled is broken.
2. Did you know that ____________________ used to be a town here?
3. I heard that ____________________ parents are taking them to a movie.
4. Our dog is ____________________ in the shack.
5. Let's swim in that big pool over ____________________.
6. Maybe we can use ____________________ swimming pool.
7. I'm sure____________________ are a lot of people in this city.
8. I wonder if they found ____________________ books yet.
9. All of the animals are over ____________________.
10. Maybe ____________________ grandparents aren't coming this year.
11. He was surprised that ____________________ were so many books in the library!
12. The last time I saw them, they were over ____________________.
13. I think ____________________ dog is lost.
14. Would you rather play here or ____________________?
15. They said ____________________ new teacher is really funny!
16. They couldn't believe ____________________ eyes!
17. The paper is kept over ____________________.
18. I wonder if ____________________ trip is going well.
19. I live right ____________________.
20. Do you know why ____________________ mom won't let them come over?

Name____

Date____

There — They're — Their

1. ____________________ were five animals coming out of the forest.
2. ____________________ teeth were sharp and glittering.
3. Oh no, ____________________ coming this way!
4. But what if ____________________ noses are so good they can smell us?
5. I'm afraid ____________________ is a good chance of that.
6. ____________________ sniffing the air. Maybe they know we're here.
7. ____________________ must be something we can do.
8. ____________________ so scary looking!
9. I bet ____________________ claws are sharp!
10. ____________________ turning around and running back into the forest.
11. Something must be chasing them. Look, ____________________ it is!
12. Wow! A bear. He's right on ____________________ tracks.
13. ____________________ fast though. I bet they'll get away.
14. I'm glad they ran over ____________________ and not over here!
15. Can you hear ____________________ howls in the distance?
16. I wonder if ____________________ going to be all right.
17. I'm sure ____________________ running as fast as possible.
18. I think they'll run to ____________________ dens and hide.
19. Our car is over ____________________. Let's get out of here!
20. Oh no! I can't remember whether or not I left the keys in

    ____________________!

Name____

Date____

Threw — Through

1. She ____________________ a fit.
2. A traveler walked ____________________ the gate.
3. He ____________________ something away.
4. We were walking ____________________ the hall.
5. Let's go ____________________ your folder.
6. He ____________________ a snowball.
7. Nobody can walk ____________________ a wall.
8. Look ____________________ your book for the answer.
9. A ball came ____________________ the window.
10. My brother ____________________ the ball.
11. Voyager is soaring ____________________ space.
12. Someone burst ____________________ the door.
13. Mark ____________________ his paper away.
14. The lightning rumbled ____________________ the sky.
15. The dog ____________________ up all over the carpet.
16. She peeked ____________________ the keyhole.
17. He ____________________ the rock as far as he could.
18. You could feel the heat of the coffee ____________________ the cup.
19. They ____________________ a rope to the tired swimmer.
20. We will be traveling ____________________ Canada.

Name____

Date____

To — Two

1. I want ____________________ sing a song.
2. Mary has ____________________ cats.
3. She is going ____________________ school.
4. These ____________________ trees are the biggest.
5. The twins are ____________________ years old.
6. It is time ____________________ sleep now.
7. We are going ____________________ Grandma's house.
8. My dad likes ____________________ read the paper.
9. My dog hurt ____________________ of his feet.
10. We have ____________________ wear hats outside today.
11. I think it is going ____________________ snow.
12. She read ____________________ books yesterday.
13. We will try ____________________ call you soon.
14. My dad has ____________________ work every day.
15. They are going ____________________ get some food.
16. We came back ____________________ days ago.
17. Do you see those ____________________ birds?
18. Why do you need ____________________ do that?
19. Who wants ____________________ draw now?
20. Dad went ____________________ work.

Name____

Date____

To — Too — Two

1. You can come along, ____________________.
2. My sister turned ____________________ yesterday.
3. Let's go ____________________ the tennis game.
4. I wanted ____________________ go, but I couldn't.
5. The door was ____________________ short for adults.
6. I want ____________________ learn more about space.
7. I think there are ____________________ people here to see us.
8. Go ____________________ the corner and turn left.
9. Wait, I want to go, ____________________!
10. It's ____________________ cold to go outside.
11. Are you going ____________________ the store?
12. That hat is ____________________ big for you.
13. Your dog is barking ____________________ much. I can't sleep.
14. He lives ____________________ miles from here.
15. I ate ____________________ much last night.
16. I'm going ____________________ wash the car now.
17. Even if we leave now, we will be ____________________ late.
18. Shall I buy you a fishing pole, ____________________?
19. These ____________________ socks don't match!
20. We will need ____________________ get into teams of four.

Name____

Date____

Toad — Towed

1. Is that a frog or a ____________________?
2. Our car had to be ____________________ to the shop.
3. A ____________________ jumped onto the road.
4. The ____________________ spends most of its life on land.
5. They ____________________ the truck all the way to Texas.
6. A ____________________ has a poisonous liquid in its skin.
7. A snowmobile ____________________ the skiers up the mountain.
8. The nets were being ____________________ behind the fishing boat.
9. We had some trouble when we ____________________ the trailer over the mountain pass.
10. Touching a ____________________ does not cause warts!
11. Long ago, mules _________________ barges up and down the Erie Canal.
12. Several tugboats ____________________ the large tanker to the dock.
13. A ____________________ normally lives from one to two years.
14. The largest ____________________ is about nine inches long.
15. Two horses ___________________ the jingling sleigh through the snow.
16. A large ____________________ can lay more than 20,000 eggs!
17. A ____________________ catches insects with its long sticky tongue.
18. A male ____________________ can puff out its throat to make a sound.
19. Our large car easily ____________________ the camping trailer.
20. A small boat called a dinghy may be ___________________ behind a sailboat.

Name____

Date____

Toes — Tows

1. This big truck __________________ three or more trailers at a time.
2. He ____________________ supplies to his cabin on a sled.
3. The nails on my ___________________ need to be clipped.
4. Human ________________ have more than half of the bones in the foot.
5. The little boy ___________________ his wagon along wherever he goes.
6. He dropped a big rock right on his ____________________.
7. Be careful not to stub your ____________________!
8. I love to feel mud squeezing through my ____________________.
9. Horses have no ____________________.
10. This big truck ____________________ our boat easily.
11. I'm very pleased with how this machine ____________________ logs.
12. Another name for fingers and ____________________ is phalanges.
13. Jimmy loves sledding so much that he happily ____________________ his sled up the mountain again and again.
14. Linus ____________________ his blanket everywhere he goes.
15. A monkey's ____________________ can cling to branches.
16. This airplane ____________________ glider planes into the sky.
17. It was so cold on the mountain that his ____________________ froze.
18. It's funny how that dog ____________________ his master on walks.
19. Let's hope someone stops and ____________________ us out.
20. An ostrich is the only bird with two __________________ on each foot.

Name____

Date____

Wade — Weighed

1. The largest hailstone ____________________ more than two pounds.
2. Take your shoes off before you ____________________ in the stream.
3. The largest ostrich ____________________ 345 pounds.
4. The wood ____________________ a lot because it was wet.
5. Great blue herons used to ____________________ in that marsh.
6. Each of the books ____________________ two pounds.
7. We had to ____________________ across the stream.
8. Let’s ____________________ out to the boats.
9. The baby ____________________ seven pounds and three ounces.
10. Fishermen who ____________________ into the lake often catch more fish.
11. It was hard to ____________________ through the deep snow.
12. I rolled up my pants to ____________________ across the river, but they got wet anyway.
13. One crocodile ____________________ 2,465 pounds!
14. Would you like to swim or just ____________________?
15. Moose like to ____________________ out into the lake to eat water plants.
16. I wish I knew how much my backpack ____________________.
17. Bears ____________________ in this stream and fish for salmon.
18. Someone once found a snake that ____________________ 500 pounds!
19. The piano ____________________ so much it took six men to move it.
20. Our watermelon ____________________ more than 30 pounds!

Name____

Date____

Waist — Waste

1. This belt is too small for my ____________________.
2. It is best not to ____________________ any food.
3. She has a tiny ____________________.
4. The ____________________ of this dress is beginning to tear.
5. The ____________________ from the factory was collected and recycled.
6. The pants fit tightly around his ____________________.
7. We must reduce ____________________ and keep the world clean.
8. My grandmother says, "____________________ not, want not."
9. She thinks watching TV is a ____________________ of time.
10. The coat had a belt around the ____________________.
11. People in poor countries do not ____________________ very much.
12. Letting the faucets drip is a ____________________ of water.
13. He wore a large belt buckle at his ____________________.
14. Please don't ____________________ paper.
15. He tied a rope around his ____________________.
16. She wore a bright sash around her ____________________.
17. Too much packaging on products is a ____________________ of plastic.
18. The outlaw carried his guns low on his ____________________.
19. Clean the fish carefully so there is no ____________________.
20. I always gain weight on my ____________________.

Name____

Date____

Wait — Weight

1. She has lost a lot of __________________.
2. Please __________________ for me at the corner.
3. I just can't __________________ until my birthday.
4. Up to half of a person's __________________ is muscles.
5. You will gain __________________ if you eat too much.
6. Did you know your __________________ can be measured three ways?
7. People in some countries must __________________ in line for almost everything.
8. The doctor told him to do something about his __________________.
9. We will __________________ and see what happens.
10. The eagle perched on a tree to __________________ for his dinner.
11. I couldn't __________________ much longer.
12. Why do we have to __________________ so long to see the doctor?
13. The boxer's __________________ was just right for the fight.
14. A lot of people must watch their __________________.
15. The travelers had to __________________ for hours at the border.
16. He held the box in his hand, trying to guess its __________________.
17. The operator made me __________________ on hold for ten minutes.
18. The nurse checked my __________________.
19. The baby is gaining __________________ every day.
20. Please be there on time. We won't be able to __________________.

Name____

Date____

Way — Weigh

1. An elephant can ____________________ as much as 6.5 tons.
2. Could you please show me the ____________________ to the store?
3. I don’t think this is the right ____________________ to do this.
4. Those dogs ____________________ about 70 pounds each.
5. There’s no ____________________ that could happen!
6. I ____________________ about 15 pounds more than I did last year.
7. About how much does a hummingbird ____________________?
8. Believe me! This is the very best ____________________ to travel.
9. An ostrich egg can ____________________ more than 3.5 pounds.
10. There must be a better ____________________ to do this!
11. Let’s ____________________ your fish!
12. Often there is more than one ____________________ to do things.
13. I’m sure you’ll think of a ____________________.
14. Which ____________________ is the campground from here?
15. I ____________________ myself every day.
16. These bags ____________________ too much for me to carry.
17. I don’t know the ____________________ to your house.
18. Most human brains ____________________ about three pounds.
19. I think we can get there this ____________________.
20. We use scales to ____________________ things.

Name____

Date____

Weak — Week

1. I was sick last ____________________.
2. The man's illness made him very ____________________.
3. This has been the best ____________________ of my entire life!
4. We went to Grandma's for a ____________________ last Thanksgiving.
5. The poor cat was too ____________________ to get up.
6. Next ____________________, I am going to a party.
7. It will take at least a ____________________ to finish the roof.
8. The boy looked pale and ____________________.
9. She felt ____________________ when she saw the blood.
10. Next ____________________ we will go shopping together.
11. There are seven days in a ____________________.
12. My father was ____________________ after he came back from the hospital.
13. It's been a long ____________________.
14. The ____________________ went so slowly, it seemed like a year.
15. The stray dog was ____________________ with hunger.
16. Last ____________________ I got a perfect score in spelling.
17. We will learn to play basketball this ____________________.
18. I felt very ____________________ this morning.
19. It is only one ____________________ until vacation!
20. She was still ____________________ when she got out of bed.

Name____

Date____

Weather — Whether

1. I don't know ____________________ she is interested or not.
2. The ____________________ report called for clear skies.
3. We usually have rainy ____________________ here in the summertime.
4. It all depends on ____________________ my homework is done in time.
5. Will you please tell me ____________________ you are planning to go?
6. The ____________________ has been terrible this winter.
7. No one knows why the ____________________ has been so bad lately.
8. I don't know ____________________ you are angry at me or not.
9. Ask Dad ____________________ he'd rather drive or fly.
10. I really hope the ____________________ will improve.
11. Let's talk about ____________________ to go camping tomorrow.
12. Ask your mom ____________________ you can come with us.
13. The ____________________ has been beautiful for two weeks.
14. I'm not sure ____________________ he's sick or just very tired.
15. The ____________________ forecast called for snow and wind.
16. Do you know ____________________ you'll be coming to visit us this summer?
17. I hope the ____________________ will be nice when we're at the beach.
18. It will happen ____________________ we like it or not.
19. The ____________________ in the mountains is often windy.
20. I'm not sure ____________________ this will make a difference.

Name____

Date____

Were — We're

1. There ____________________ twenty animals on the mountain.
2. I think ____________________ going to be late.
3. The children ____________________ all falling asleep.
4. I'm not sure what ____________________ going to do now.
5. He said ____________________ welcome to come anytime.
6. They ____________________ planning a big trip in April.
7. I hope ____________________ next.
8. Where ____________________ you when I called?
9. The birds ____________________ gathering seeds.
10. I wonder if ____________________ really ready for an emergency.
11. Who ____________________ those men?
12. I guess ____________________ going out for dinner again.
13. They think ____________________ dangerous, don't they?
14. How ____________________ your parents?
15. Three of the horses ____________________ dying.
16. What ____________________ his reasons for changing his mind?
17. It's nice to know ____________________ always welcome here.
18. Three little cabins ____________________ hidden in the woods.
19. I'm glad ____________________ moving now.
20. She's sure that ____________________ going to be lucky this time.

Name____

Date____

Where — Were

1. ____________________ are you going?
2. The cats ____________________ asleep on the rug.
3. Who ____________________ those people?
4. ____________________ did you learn about the new rules?
5. They ____________________ planning to go to the beach.
6. ____________________ you at school yesterday?
7. ____________________ are my books? I must have lost them.
8. I couldn't tell if they ____________________ telling the truth.
9. We ____________________ planning to go swimming, but it rained.
10. ____________________ is everybody today?
11. All of the children ____________________ asleep.
12. Can anyone tell me ____________________ to go now?
13. Last week my legs ____________________ very weak.
14. This is ____________________ I saw the strange person.
15. ____________________ you eating those cookies?
16. There ____________________ several games going on at once.
17. ____________________ does it say that?
18. The books ____________________ stacked in a neat pile.
19. Mark knows ____________________ your backpack is hidden.
20. Let me know ____________________ you would like to sit.

Name____

Date____

Which — Witch

1. Do you know ____________________ house belongs to the Smiths?
2. I dressed up as a ____________________ at Halloween.
3. For Mother's Day, I bought Mom a kitchen ____________________.
4. ____________________ kind of cake do you want for your birthday?
5. I am not sure ____________________ person I should see about this.
6. A ____________________ is supposed to ride on a broom.
7. ____________________ bus am I supposed to take?
8. Please tell me ____________________ record you want to play.
9. A ____________________ was soaring through the sky.
10. ____________________ day of the week is your favorite?
11. The lady next door pretends to be a ____________________.
12. ____________________ kind of ice cream do you want?
13. Could you tell me ____________________ way to go now?
14. The ____________________ had a black cat.
15. ____________________ way is the library?
16. ____________________ restaurant is your favorite?
17. My sister dressed up as a ____________________ for the party.
18. ____________________ way are you going?
19. I'm not sure ____________________ coat I really want.
20. A ____________________ is supposed to have evil powers.

Name____

Date____

Whose — Who's

1. ____________________ our new neighbor?
2. ____________________ boots are these in the middle of the floor?
3. ____________________ wig is this?
4. We didn't know ____________________ lunch it was.
5. I wonder ____________________ coming for dinner.
6. ____________________ coming to the store with me?
7. ____________________ desk am I sitting on?
8. ____________________ that man over there behind the chair?
9. ____________________ coat is still on the rack?
10. ____________________ sneakers are those?
11. ____________________ going to spend the night with you?
12. ____________________ coming to the party?
13. ____________________ mink coat is this?
14. ____________________ going to the movies?
15. Would you please find out ____________________ going by bus?
16. I can't tell ____________________ dog this is.
17. ____________________ watch am I wearing?
18. ____________________ house is that?
19. I wonder ____________________ going to get the best grade.
20. I don't know ____________________ keys these are.

Name____

Date____

Wood — Would

1. This fireplace is for burning ____________________ only.
2. I ____________________ like to invite you to my party.
3. He liked to chop ____________________ in the deep winter.
4. The ____________________ was too wet to burn.
5. Nobody ____________________ help the old woman at first.
6. I ____________________ if I could but I can't so I won't.
7. A squirrel lives in that pile of ____________________.
8. This ____________________ be a lot easier if we read the directions.
9. He ____________________ have come, but he was sick.
10. Please go fetch some ____________________.
11. They ____________________ like to come with us.
12. The furniture was carved from ____________________.
13. Most paper is made from ____________________.
14. We ____________________ like to go to Florida this winter.
15. I ____________________ come tomorrow, but I have a dance lesson.
16. Almost anyone ____________________ be happy if they won a contest.
17. This ____________________ is so hard a nail won't go through it.
18. Why ____________________ anyone say something like that?
19. The house was built completely out of ____________________.
20. The artist is using ____________________ to carve a statue.

Name______________________________

Date______________________________

Your — You're

1. ____________________ mother is pretty, and she is a good cook!
2. Did you say ____________________ staying home today?
3. ____________________ Henry Cook, aren't you?
4. Why aren't you in ____________________ room?
5. ____________________ birthday is April 3, isn't it?
6. Is that ____________________ boat?
7. ____________________ in the second grade.
8. ____________________ the winner!
9. ____________________ cat is in my garden again.
10. Is this ____________________ hat?
11. Is it true that ____________________ the fastest runner?
12. ____________________ going to be late if you don't hurry!
13. ____________________ bicycle is better than mine.
14. He's on his way to ____________________ house now.
15. ____________________ supposed to be working, not sleeping.
16. ____________________ dog is funny.
17. Is that ____________________ baby brother crying?
18. ____________________ going to have to do something soon!
19. Someone told me that ____________________ good at math.
20. ____________________ doing a great job!